THE WASHING MACHINE MANUAL

Revised 2nd Edition

DIY Plumbing □ Maintenance □ Repair

Graham Dixon

Haynes
®

First edition published 1988
Reprinted 1988, 1989, 1990, 1991
Revised Second Edition
published 1992
Reprinted 1993 (twice)
Reprinted 1994

Published by:
Haynes Publishing,
Sparkford, Nr Yeovil, Somerset
BA22 7JJ, England

**British Library Cataloguing in
Publication Data**

A catalogue record for this book
is available from the British
Library.

ISBN 1 85010 860 9 (Book Trade)
ISBN 1 85010 863 3 (Motor Trade)

Printed in Great Britain by
J. H. Haynes & Co. Ltd.

**While every effort is taken to
ensure the accuracy of the
information given in this book,
no liability can be accepted by
the author or publishers for any
loss, damage or injury caused
by errors in, or omissions from,
the information given.**

Contents

Introduction

Today's modern automatic washing machines are the highly refined offspring of their predecessors. Many of the refinements have been made to aid production and to cut production costs for the manufacturer, although it is fair to say that improvements to washing and spin speeds have also been incorporated. The automatic washing machine has changed little in its basic operation over the years, apart from the obvious cosmetic changes and additions of faster spin speeds and increased wash variations. These changes have not significantly increased the overall cost of automatic machines in real terms, they are actually cheaper now than twenty five years ago. With the use of electronics to control motor speeds and the high demand for machines, mass production techinques and a competitive market have kept costs relatively low.

The main drawback has been in the cost of repairs and servicing your appliance once the guarantee has expired. Many people have opted for the five year cover offered by manufacturers only to find that in some cases the defective part only is covered and not the wear and tear, and in particular, not the labour charge for fitting the replacement part. This often results in a small repair, e.g. replacement of a belt, still costing around £45. The breakdown of which is the cost of the belt, approximately £5, is waivered, but the call-out and repair charge of £40 or more, plus VAT, is levied.

This book looks at the automatic washing machine in detail and its aim is to help you to understand the function and operation of the internal components of your machine with the view to assist you in finding the fault and the knowledge to repair it.

Flowcharts, diagrams and step-by-step photographic sequences have been used to create a logical pattern to fault finding. This enables the reader to follow a sequence of events in theory (using the flowcharts) in practise (using the photographic sequences) and in detail using the diagrams.

Approached in a logical step-by-step manner, not as a haphazard guess, most if not all faults are within the capabilities of the DIY person. The book is best read cover to cover to gain the gist of flowchart use and to familiarise yourself with procedures and the best ways to locate and rectify faults that may occur. You can then use the book as a quick reference guide before and during repairs. It is impossible to deal specifically with any particular machine as models very considerably with each manufacturer having their own style of pumps, hoses, bearing sizes, etc., but the concept of an automatic washer differs very little between manufacturers. This will become apparent after reading through the book.

Having read the book, you will become more aware of safety around the home owing to a better understanding of your electrical items and their limitations. Regular checks for faults which can be rectified prior to failure or accident greatly increase the safety of your appliances. You will also gain more efficient use of your items through understanding their correct operation.

The machines in the photo sequences have been selected as a cross section of some of the most popular ones found in homes today. Both old and new machines are used in the sequences to highlight actual fault areas and faults to look out for. All names and model numbers are used for customer reference purposes only. At all times, before working on a machine, make sure that it is isolated from both the electrical supply, i.e. switch off socket and remove plug, and from the water supply by turning off the feed taps. This ensures your safety and that of the machine.

We hope you will use this manual to asist you in the Do It Yourself repair of your machine. With most repairs you will find it speedier than calling a repair company, and at the same time save the added burden of call-out and labour charges that repair companies must charge to cover overheads and operating costs.

With this in mind, we hope that your faults are few and far between, but remember... prevention is better than cure, and regular checks and servicing of your machine can prevent any bigger problems arising in the future.

Acknowledgements

The author would like to extend his thanks and gratitude to the following poeple and organisations for their help in the compilation of certain sections.

Oracstar Ltd.
Lever Bros.
Crabtree Electrical Industries Ltd.

Thanks also to Andrew Morland for the photographic work.

Chapter 1

Emergency procedures

With such symptoms as leaking; flooding; unusual noises; blowing fuses, etc., it is best to carry out the following procedure. It is essential that the machine is NOT allowed to continue its programme until the fault has been located and rectified.

Firstly – Do Not Panic

(a) Isolate the machine from the mains supply. That is, turn the machine off, switch off at the wall socket, and remove the plug from the socket.

(b) Turn off the Hot and Cold taps that the fill hoses of the machine connect to. This is done because, even with the power turned off, if a valve is at fault, it may be jammed in the open position. The machine will still fill, as turning the power or the machine off will make no difference to this type of fault.

(c) At this point, the power and water should be disconnected. Even now, if there is still water in the machine, it could still be leaking. Any water that may still be in the machine can be extracted from the machine by syphoning. This is easily done by lifting the outlet hose from its usual position, and lowering it

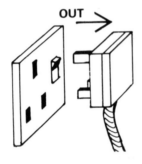

OUT →

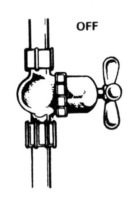

OFF

DRAIN

below the level of water in the machine. This will allow the water to drain (unless of course, there is a blockage in the outlet hose!). The easiest method is if the outlet hose will reach to an outside door, where all that is needed is a little movement and the water should drain. Alternatively, the water can be caught in a bucket using the same technique to drain the water. To stop the water lift the pipe above the height of the machine. Repeat this process until the machine is empty.

(d) Do not open the door to remove the clothes until all of the previous steps have been carried out, and a few minutes

have elapsed to allow the clothes in the machine to cool. In cases where the machine was on a very hot wash, wait about half an hour. When all of these steps have been carried out, and the clothes have been removed from the drum, it is then possible to calmly sit down and start to work out what the problem may be, and form the plan of attack in a logical and concise manner.

Chapter 2

A General Safety Guide

Most people have a healthy respect for electricity and understand its potential assets as well as the way it can be dangerous, sometimes lethal, if taken for granted and misused.

Electricity at all voltages is to be respected. Those that do not observe the basic rules of electricity are not only a danger to themselves but to those around them. Electrical accidents should be regarded as avoidable. Most are due to plain carelessness and the failure to follow basic rules of electricity even when they are already known.

There are in the region of sixteen million homes in Britain supplied with electriciy, each home having on average twenty-five electrical appliances. With such a volume of items, it may be a surprise to find that fatalities due to electrical accidents are less than eighty per year. Although this is a small percentage figure in terms of population and only represents 1 per cent of the 8,000 deaths resulting from accidents in the home, the figure is still too high.

The three most common causes of shock or fires from electrical appliances are:

1. Faulty wiring of the appliances, i.e. frayed or damaged flex or cable, incorrect fuse, poor socket, poor/damaged plug, incorrectly wired plug, etc.
2. Misuse of the appliance. The combination of water and electricity greatly increases the possibility of injury.
3. Continuing to use an electrical appliance knowing it to be unsafe, for example with a cracked casing, faulty plug, damaged cable, faulty on/off switch, etc.

By having the awareness of the need for safety, several of the above faults are avoidable. Others can be eliminated by regular inspection and immediate correction of faults, failure or wear. As for misuse, this may be due to a purely foolhardy approach or genuine ignorance of danger. This can be overcome by understanding and, above all, acting upon the guidelines in this book. If at anytime you feel you lack the ability to do a particular job yourself, then it is best not to try. You can still carry out the diagnosis of the problem thus enusuring that any work carried out by a repair company is correct. This alone can sometimes save much time and expense.

DO'S
• Thoroughly read all the information in this book prior to putting it into practice.
• Isolate any appliance before repair or inspection commences.
• Correctly fit the mains plug (*see:* Plugs and Sockets), ensuring the connections are in the correct position, tight and the cord clamp fitted on the outer insulation of the cable.
• Check that the socket used is in good condition and has a sound earth path (*see* Basics – Electrical).
• Take time to consider the problem at hand and allow enough time to complete the job without rushing.
• Follow a methodical approach to the stripdown of the item and make notes. This helps greatly with reassembly.
• Double-check everything.
• Ask or seek help if in doubt.

DON'TS
• Do not work on any machine that is still plugged in even if the socket switch is **OFF**. Always isolate fully – **PLUG OUT**.

- Do not in **ANY** circumstances repair damaged flex or cables with insulation tape.
- Do not sacrifice safety by affecting a temporary repair.

GENERAL

Consider your own safety and that of other people.

Act in a way that prevents incidents from becoming accidents.

Use your common sense and think before acting.

Tidy workplaces make safer workplaces.

Identify hazards.

Observe the rule of Safety First.

Never underestimate the dangers.

Switch off! Always withdraw plug and disconnect from mains.

Appliances vary – make sure you have a suitable replacement part.

For screws use a screwdriver, for nuts a spanner, for knurled nuts use pliers.

Examine and clean all connections before fitting new parts.

Tighten firmly all screws and nuts.

Your safety depends on these simple rules.

Fuses: Up to 250 watts 1 amp; 750 watts 3 amp; 750 to 3000 watts 13 amp.

Insulation is for your protection. Don't interfere.

Renew worn or damaged appliance flex.

Secure flex clamps and all protective covers.

Test physically and electrically on completion.

Ensure that only the correct rated fused is used. It is dangerous to exceed the required rating. Even if the appliance appears to work normally little or no protection will be afforded should a fault occur.

Plug wiring

Plug wiring must be connected according to the following code to ensure safety. The colours are as follows:

Live – Brown (or Red), symbol 'L'
Neutral – Blue (or Black), symbol 'N'
Earth – Green/Yellow (or Green), symbol 'E'

The colours in brackets are those used until the newer and current international standards were introduced. They may still be found on some equipment. Plug terminals are identified either by colour (old or new) or by the letter symbols shown.

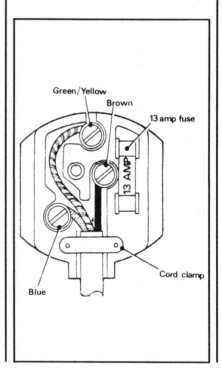

Chapter 3

Basics – Electrical

For the sake of safety around the home or office, a basic understanding of electricity is essential. Even if you don't intend to carry out any repairs or servicing of your appliances yourself, a sound understanding of household electrical supply will prove invaluable in the long run. Ignorance is no protection against either your or a third party's errors, whether it be on repairs, servicing or the installation of appliances. It is with this in mind that this chapter has been written. It is not an in-depth study of the subject – there are many books that contain more detailed information for those who want to know more about electricity.

In this instance, the aim is to impart a safe knowledge without too much technical data. Some may argue that a little knowledge is a dangerous thing, but I believe that total ignorance is a much greater danger. To be informed is to be enlightened – to be aware of danger helps one to avoid it and to understand how and why certain safety criteria should be adopted.

Figure 1 shows a simplified, but typical household supply. The substation has power supplied to it at very high voltage (400,000 volts) in three-phase form. This supply is converted at the substation, via a transformer, down to 240 volt single-phase and is then

distributed to our homes. In normal circumstances, current flows from the live supply of the substation's transformer, through the electrical items being used in the house and back via the neutral conductor (cable) to the substation transformer's neutral pole (a closed loop). The neutral terminal of the transformer is in turn connected to the ground (earth – meaning in this case, the general mass of the earth), as shown in Figure 2. It is usual to use the armoured sheath of the electricity supply authority's cable in order to provide a low impedance continuous link back to the supply transformers' start

Fig 1. Typical household supply.

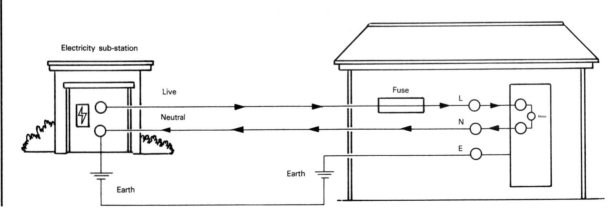

Electricity sub-station

Live

Neutral

Fuse

L

N

E

Motor

Earth

Earth

Fig. 2

Earth path if fault occurs.

Result of high resistance or break in normal earth path. Fault will find path of least resistance.

point. Various types of earthing can be encountered: connection to the armoured sheath of the authority's supply cable; own earth rod; transformer earth rod via general mass of the earth; or the increasingly popular neutral conductor of the authority's supply cable (often called PME – protective multiple earthing or TN-C-S system).

The earth loop path is designed to encourage current to flow, in the event of an earth fault, to enable the protective devices within the consumer unit (fuse, MCB or RCD) to operate in order to isolate the supply to the circuit. Failure to cause the protective device to operate will result in the appliance remaining live with the consequence that any person touching the appliance will receive a nasty, possibly fatal, electric shock.

Remember, electricity always takes the route of least resistance, therefore a person standing on the ground touching a live appliance can provide a low resistance alternative earth path resulting in a severe shock or worse. For this reason, the resistance of the earth loop path must be low enough to allow sufficient fault current to flow to operate the protective fuse or circuit breaker.

The term used for testing earthing performance is earth loop impedance, which means checking to see if the current flow is impeded and if it is, by how much. This test requires a specialised meter giving resistance figures in ohms, the maximum reading recommended by the IEE (Institution of Electrical Engineers) being 1.1 ohms for a domestic earth

path, unless a Type 1 MCB is in circuit in which case a 2 ohm maximum is permissible.

NOTE: A correct test cannot be carried out using a low voltage meter because a fault can exist that allows the low voltage of, say, 9 volts to pass easily (e.g. just one tiny strand of wire poorly connected) but would break down and go high-resistance or open-circuit if a working voltage of 240 v at 13 amps was applied. Though low voltage testing will give an indication of earth path, it cannot indicate quality. The earth loop impedance meter gives a clearer indication of earth quality under more realistic conditions.

What is an earth fault?

An earth fault is defined as the

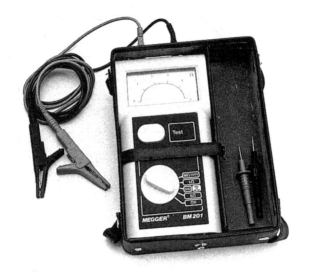

A versatile test meter incorporating 500v insulation test facility.

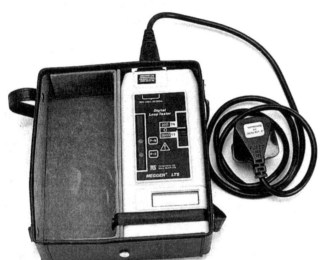

A professional earth loop test meter gives the only true indication of the earth path quality.

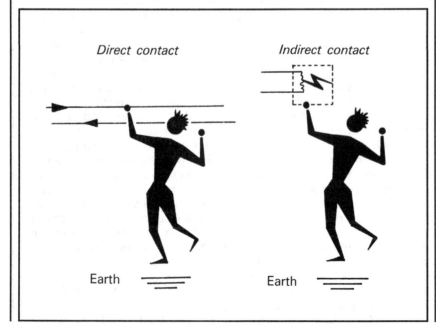

Direct contact

Indirect contact

Earth

Earth

condition where electricity flows to earth when in normal circumstances, it should not do so. There are two recognised ways in which this may happen: direct and indirect.

Direct. When contact is made directly with the current-carrying conductor which is designed to carry that current.

Indirect. Touching a part of an appliance, that would not normally carry current but is doing so due to a fault.

What is a consumer unit?

The consumer unit is where the supply into the house is split into separate circuits, i.e. those for lights, sockets, etc. It houses a

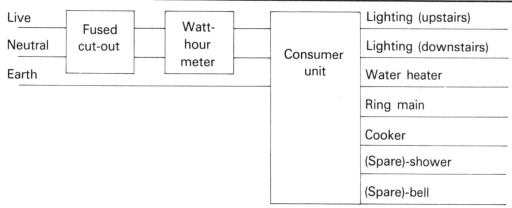

Live			Lighting (upstairs)
Neutral	Fused cut-out	Watt-hour meter	Lighting (downstairs)
Earth		Consumer unit	Water heater
			Ring main
			Cooker
			(Spare)-shower
			(Spare)-bell

A typical house insulation.

main isolation switch or combined RCD which is used to isolate (remove power from) all the circuits in the house. Also housed within the unit are various fuse-carriers for cartridge or rewirable fuses or a Miniature Circuit Breaker (MCB) in place of fuses. Each circuit leading from the consumer unit has its own rating of fuse or MCB and only that fuse rating and no other

must be used. NOTE: Even when the consumer unit is switched off there is still a live supply to it. Do not remove the covers of the consumer unit or tackle any inspection or repair to this item without seeking further information. Faults other than fuse renewal are best left to skilled electrical engineers. Although assistance may be available from other publications, extreme care should be exercised. As mentioned earlier,

it is not the aim of this book to invite the repair or maintenance of items that are not fully isolated.

All about fuses

As mentioned earlier, two versions of fuses are to be found: the cartridge type and the rewirable type. The rewirable type is difficult and fiddly to rewire and the cartridge type, although easier to renew, is often difficult to obtain. Both these systems have drawbacks in being awkward and not very 'user friendly'.

An ordinary fuse is simply a weak link designed to break at a preset rating. If a circuit is overloaded or a short circuit occurs, the resulting overload will cause the fuse to melt and sever the supply. Unless a direct short circuit occurs, however, the overload on the fuse may not be enough to cause the fuse to blow because it has a fair degree of leeway over its rating value. It, therefore, offers only basic safety and will not afford any personal safety as the time taken to break is usually too long.

To the old familiar imperial ratings for fuses and circuit breakers have now been added the international Renard ratings. A complete changeover will eventually be effected for common market standardization.

Fuse manufacturers are still using the imperial sizes whilst circuit breaker manufacturers have mostly changed to the new

Typical older-style consumer unit with isolation switch and wired fuses only.

Modern consumer unit with RCD main switch and MCBs on all circuits.

ratings. An equivalence chart is shown below:

Current Rating

Imp.	Renard	Typical Circuit
5	6	Lighting
10	10	
15	16	1 mm. htr
20	20	
30	32	Ring main
45	40	Cooker/ shower

Miniature Circuit Breakers

The miniature circuit breaker (MCB) is now widely used and overcomes all the problems associated with ordinary fuses. The MCB is a small sophisticated unit that affords a much higher degree of protection than an ordinary fuse. It is tamper-proof and the unit involved is easily identified when one has tripped (switch moves to 'OFF' position). Most importantly, MCBs cannot be reset if the fault still exists which eliminates the practice of putting in the wrong fuse wire or cartridge to get things working – a foolish and most dangerous practice! MCBs are available in similar ratings to ordinary fuses

and operate in two ways. Referring to the accompanying photograph, current flows into the unit at 'H1' and along 'G' through coil 'E1' and on to the moving contact 'D' (shown here open circuit). Contact 'D' in the ON position would be resting on fixed contact 'C' and so current would flow to H2.

Two fault conditions may arise; firstly, short circuit. This type of fault would quickly increase the current flow through the unit. Section E1, being a coil would increase its magnetic field and as a result attract E2 into the coil centre. This action trips the mechanism arm 'F' and causes 'C – D' to open circuit. Conductor 'A' and arc chamber 'B' act to supress the arc formed on the contact point. This is

Mechanism of miniature circuit breaker.
A. Arc runner
B. Arc chamber
C. Fixed contact
D. Moving contact
E1. Solenoid coil
E2. Moving core
F. Trip bar
G. Thermo-metal
H1. Wiring terminal
H2. Wiring terminal
I. Fixing

done by the arc runners drawing the arc across the arc chamber where it is chopped into small arcs which are quickly extinguished. The action of the MCB is much quicker than an ordinary fuse wire. The second type of fault could simply be an overload on the circuit and, although exceeding the safe working load of the circuit, it would not cause the solenoid to trip. In this type of situation, the current flowing through 'G' causes the conductor to heat up. The conductor is made of a tri-metal plate that bends when heated. The bending action of the conductor trips arm 'F', causing 'C' and 'D' to open circuit as before. This operation again is much better than fuse wire and calibration to higher tolerances is possible.

NOTE: These units are factory-calibrated to extremely accurate tolerances and must not be tampered with nor attempts made to readjust them. The internal workings are only shown to help understand their operation. In the event of faults or failures, a new replacement unit must be fitted. No repair or adjustment is possible.

Unfortunately, neither fuses nor miniature circuit breakers alone can give protection to anyone involved in a DIRECT EARTH situation. Indeed, the same can apply in the case of an INDIRECT EARTH contact. This may sound confusing, but it should be realised that in a 'direct contact' situation a person is literally shorting out Live and Earth, whereas in an indirect contact situation, the Live to Earth path is already there because the equipment itself is connected to earth. The reason the fuse hasn't blown or the circuit breaker tripped is because the fault is not great enough to operate the safety mechanism, yet is great enough to be fatal. For instance, a 10 amp fuse would never blow with an 8 amp earth fault on the circuit, yet 8 amps constitutes a very

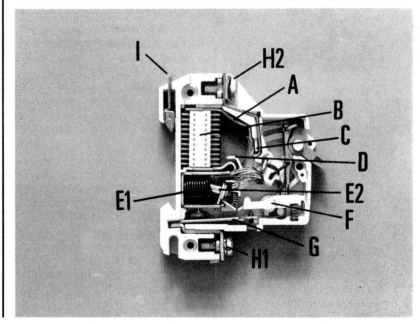

dangerous level of earth fault current.

Residual Current Devices

To afford a higher degree of protection, another device has been developed, available in various forms.
1. Mounted within the consumer unit to protect all or selected circuits.
2. As individual socket protection.
3. An adaptor to be used as portable protection and used where required.

The name given to this device in all its forms is the Residual Current Device (RCD). It may also be called a Residual Current Circuit Breaker (RCCB). In the early days of its introduction, it was known as an Earth Leakage Circuit Breaker (ELCB).

The primary protection is the integrity of the earthing, RCDs, in addition to the earthing, provide a much higher degree of protection depending upon the degree of sensitivity. For personal protection it is recommended that a sensitivity of 30 mA is used.

It is generally considered that an earth fault of 1A or more is a fire risk, 50 mA or more provides a shock risk which can have varying effects upon the human body depending upon the value of earth fault current and the body resistance of the person and, of course, their state of health. The heartbeat cycle is about 0.75 second. It is therefore necessary to cut off the fault current in less than one cardiac cycle. The Wiring Regulations stipulate that for Indirect Contact protection isolation must occur within 0.4 second.

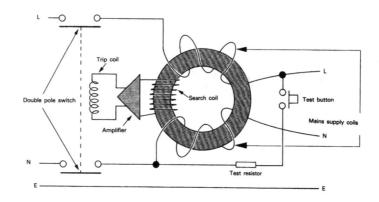

A simplified RCD circuit.

How does an RCD work?

An RCD protects by constantly monitoring the current flowing in the live and neutral wires supplying a circuit or an individual item of equipment. In normal circumstances the current flowing in the two wires is equal but, when an earth leakage occurs due to a fault or an accident, an imbalance occurs and this is detected by the RCD which automatically cuts off the power in a split second.

To be effective, the RCD must operate very quickly and a low earth fault current. Those most frequently recommended are designed to detect earth leakage faults in excess of 30 mA (30/1000 of an amp) and to disconnect the power supply within 200 ms (the rated sensitivity); these limits are well inside the safety margin within which electrocution or fire would not be expected to occur.

It should now be apparent that RCDs are designed to sever mains current should your

electrical appliance malfunction electrically, or should you cut through the mains cable of your lawnmower for instance. They are simply a fail-safe device and should be used as such. In my opinion, used correctly they are an invaluable asset to your household.

NOTE: The use of an RCD must be in addition to normal overlod protection, i.e. fuses or MCBs, and not instead of it. All residual current devices have a test button facility. It is essential that this is tested regularly to verify that the device operates. For use with adaptors or sockets, or for outside use, test before each operation. If failure occurs (does not trip, or trip appears sluggish or hard to obtain) have the unit tested immediately. This will require an RCD test meter and is best left to a qualified electrician.

The RCD units shown were kindly provided by Crabtree Electrical Industries Ltd., Walsall, West Midlands. All the units manufactured by them are made to the highest possible standards.

Chapter 4

Basics – Plumbing

Although the machine may have been working correctly for some time in its present position, incorrect installation of a machine may cause faults many months later. Because of this time span, the faults are not associated with bad plumbing and can cause the D.I.Y. engineer to look for other faults, which is very time consuming and annoying. Having said this, it is therefore worth a few minutes examining the existing pipework, and checking the manufacturer's installation details. These details will be found in the manufacturer's booklet that came with the machine. Even if the installation of your machine was left to an "expert", it is still advisable to read this section, as the chances are that they will not have read the installation details either!

For those of you who cannot find the manufacturer's booklet, what follows is a brief description of plumbing requirements that apply to nearly all automatic dishwashers and washing machines, and the reasons why they should be observed.

If the machine is to be plumbed in 'Hot and Cold', then isolation taps must be fitted.

This enables the water supply to be cut off (isolated) between the normal house supply and that of the washer. **Note**: The rubber hoses connected to the isolation taps should be positioned so that they don't get trapped when the machine is pushed back, or rub against any rough surfaces during the machine's operation. Both of these conditions can cause the pipe to wear, due to the slight movement of the machine when in use. Also ensure that no loops have been formed in the hot inlet hose. In the beginning this will not cause any trouble, but as the pipe gets older and the hot water takes effect, the pipe will soften and a kink will form. This will then cause a restriction or complete stoppage of water to the machine. This can also happen to the cold inlet hose, although it is very rare, owing to the increased pressure in the cold system.

The next thing to do, is check that there is adequate water pressure to operate the hot and cold valves, (see also *Functional Testing*). On hot and cold machines, select a hot-only fill. the machine should fill to working level within four minutes. The same should apply when a rinse cycle has been

selected. This gives a rough indication that the water pressure is adequate to open and close the valves. This is because the valves are pressure-operated and a 4 p.s.i. minimum is required for their correct operation, (see *Water Inlet Valves*). The cold pressure is usually governed by the outside mains pressure, but the hot water pressure is governed by the height of the hot water tank or its header tank.

Problems can arise when the tanks are less than eight feet higher than the water valve they are supplying. This is often found in bungalows and some flats. If a slow fill is suspected, check the small filter that can be found inside the hot and cold valves, when the inlet hose is unscrewed. These can be removed and cleaned by simply pulling them out gently with pliers. Care must be taken not to damage the filter or allow any small particles to get passed when you remove it. Clean water is normally supplied to the valves, but in many cases old pipework or the limescale deposits from boilers, etc., can collect at these points.

Kinks and loops can also affect the outlet pipe and cause

several problems to the wash, rinse and spin programmes.

Outlet hose

The outlet hose MUST fit into a pipe larger than itself, thus giving an 'Air Brake' to eliminate syphoning. The height of the outlet hose is also important if syphoning is to be avoided. Syphoning can occur when the end of the outlet hose is below the level of water in the machine, which would result in the machine emptying at the same time as filling, and if the machine were to be turned off, would continue to empty the water from the machine, down to its syphon level.

Syphoning is a common fault and can give rise to some unexpected faults, such as:-

Failing to start to wash (always filling).

Excessive filling time.

Programme failing to advance through rinses.

Washing times longer than normal.

The following diagrams show correct and incorrect plumbing techniques, which will cause and cure any syphoning. This also shows that some of the 'major' faults that appear, can be attributed to something as simple as syphoning and can be cured almost immediately.

All of the above faults can be attributed to syphoning, although this may not be the only cause.

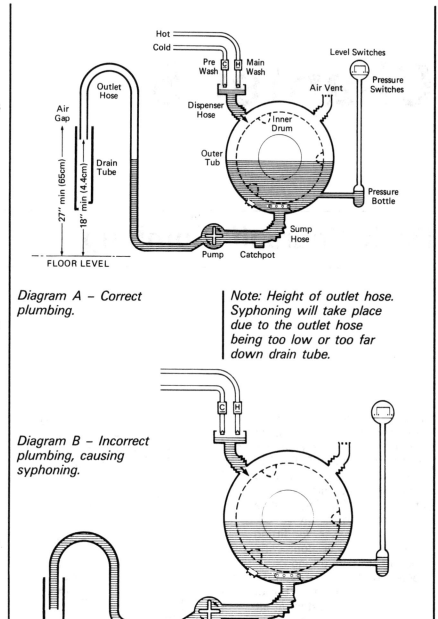

Diagram A – Correct plumbing.

Note: Height of outlet hose. Syphoning will take place due to the outlet hose being too low or too far down drain tube.

Diagram B – Incorrect plumbing, causing syphoning.

Chapter 5

Do It Yourself Plumbing

When a machine is to be fitted in close proximity to an existing sink unit, you can take advantage of the new style 'SELFBORE' taps and outlet systems now available. These simple and effective D.I.Y. fittings will save both time and money.

In most cases, the fitting of these taps can be done with only a screwdriver and no soldering is required. You do not even need to drain or turn off the main water system at all.

At this stage, I feel it is better to give you some visual help rather than pages of text. The following pages show you how easy the fitting of such units can be!

①  First, unscrew tap and open clamp.

② Fit clamp around copper pipe in required position. Make sure washer is in position.

③ 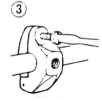 Engage screw and tighten until clamp is secure. Do not over tighten

④ Insert tap assembly into clamp. Ensure tap is in 'off' position.

⑤  Turn clockwise until pipe is penetrated. Set tap to position required.

⑥ 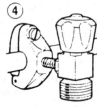 Tighten hexagonal nut towards the pipe. This secures tap in position.

⑦ 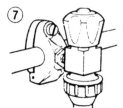 The tap is now ready for use. Connect hose to ¾ BSP thread on tap and turn on.

Plumbing in.

Self Plumbing out

Method of fitting

(1) Select the most convenient place in the waste pipe 1¼" (31mm) or 1½" (38mm) dia.
2. Disconnect components (as shown above). Place saddle halves around waste pipe, removing saddle inserts if pipe is 1½" dia. Ensure that 'O' ring is seated in recess. Tighten screws by stages to give an even and maximum pressure on waste pipe.
3. Insert cutting tool and screw home (clockwise) until hole is cut in waste pipe. Repeat to ensure a clean entry.
4. Remove cutter and screw in elbow. Use locking nut ⑤ to determine final position of elbow and tighten, or screw non-return valve ③ directly into saddle piece.
5. To complete installation, choose correct size hose

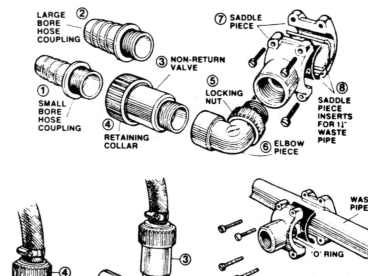

Discharge into a combined sink and washing machine trap.

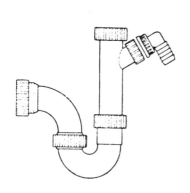

This trap allows water from the sink to drain away as normal but has an extra branch for attaching the washing machine hose.

Fitting instructions for washing machine/dishwasher drain kit.

coupling to suit drain hose and secure hose with hose clip (not included).
* It is important to remove regularly lint and other deposits from non-return valve. Simply unscrew retaining collar ④
This information has been kindly supplied by *ORACSTAR*, a leader in the field of Self Plumbing kits, whose wide range of D.I.Y. fittings and accessories can be found in most leading D.I.Y. stores.

This unit provides an in line air break to prevent syphonage occurring via your appliance drain hose. Full fitting instructions are supplied with every unit.

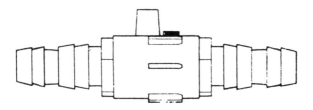

Chapter 6

Tools and Equipment

Modern automatic washing machines do not require very specialised tools. Many of the routine repairs such as blocked pumps, renewal of door seals and hoses can normally be completed with a selection of the following tools: crossblade and flatblade screwdrivers, combination pliers, simple multimeter, pliers.

Most people who are D.I.Y. orientated will own one or more of these items already. A useful addition to this selection would be a 'Mole' wrench, a socket and/or box spanner set, soft-face hammer and circlip pliers. These would help with the larger jobs, such as motor removal and bearing removal, etc.

Bearing removal/renewal and the like may also require certain things such as bearing pullers. As these can be expensive to buy, it is best to hire them from a tool hire specialist for the short period that you require them. Local garages may also be willing to let you hire them for a small deposit.

It will not prove difficult to build up a selection of tools capable of tackling the faults that you are likely to find on your machine. Most of the large D.I.Y. stores will stock the tools that you require, often at a good saving.

When buying tools check the quality; a cheap spanner or socket set is a waste of money if it bends or snaps after only a short period of use. Having said that, there are many tools on the market that are of a reasonable quality and are inexpensive. Try to buy the best that your budget will allow. Remember, the tools that you buy are a long-term investment and should give years of useful service.

As with any investment, it is wise to look after it and tools should be treated the same. Having spent time and money on tools, they should be kept in a clean and serviceable condition. Ensure that they are clean and dry before storage.

Chapter 7

Locating a Fault

Whenever possible the symptoms of the fault should be confirmed by the judicial operation of the machine up to the point of the suspected fault, using the appropriate test sequence, whereupon the machine should be stopped disconnected from the mains supply and the relevant flowchart followed. For major leaks, blown fuses, etc., this is not practical. In these cases, the fault is known and further confirmation would be of little benefit. This may in fact, result in further damage to the machine or its surroundings.

Being able to assess and locate a fault may at first seem a difficult thing to do, but if a few simple procedures are carried out prior to starting the work, they will help reduce the time spent on the machine. Hopping in a random fashion from one part of the machine to another, hoping that you will come across the fault and subsequently repair it, is hardly the best aproach to repair work. This is not the way to tackle any job. Without doubt, the best method of fault finding is to be gained from your own experience of the machine, the fault with it and its location and rectification based on all the

available information. Always remember that a methodical approach to the work in hand, saves time and effort by eliminating unnecessary replacements based on guesswork.

There are, however, a few things that can be done before such testing. These will ascertain if, in fact, it is the machine itself that is at fault or if an external/user fault is the source. Indeed, a large percentage of repair calls, are in fact, not a fault of the machine at all. Before jumping to conclusions, pause for a moment. You will not only save time and effort, but money as well.

Remember these points when starting a repair.
1. Allow yourself enough time to complete the task in hand.
2. Do not cut corners at the expense of safety.
3. Try to ensure adequate working space wherever possible.
4. Make notes about the position of the part/s to be removed, the colours and position of wires, bolts, etc.

If you can acquire this practice, it will help you in all repairs that you carry out, not only with your washing machine.

A few simple checks.
a) CHECK – that the machine is turned on at the socket.
b) CHECK – that the fuse in the plug is intact and working. This can be checked by replacing the suspected fuse with one out of a working item of the same rating.
c) CHECK – that the taps are in the ON position.
d) CHECK – that the door is closed correctly, and that a wash cycle is selected and the knob or switch has been pulled/pushed to the ON position.
e) CHECK – that the machine is not on a 'RINSE HOLD' position. This on most machines will cause the machine to stand idle until instructed to do otherwise.

If the fault still remains, the next step is to determine its true nature, and subsequent repair.

Chapter 8

General Care and Attention

For many repairs it is best that the machine is laid on its front face or side. Generally it is best to lay the machine on the side opposite the timer. (The timer is located directly behind the main programme knob.) This is to avoid the tub and drum assembly coming in contact with the timer.

Always ensure that the outer shell of the machine is protected with a suitable cover when attempting to lay the machine down. The machine should be lowered slowly, to avoid excessive movement of the suspension. When lowering the machine, it is a good idea to place a strip of wood under the top edge of the machine, to provide room for the fingers for lifting the machine back into its correct position after the repair.

When laying the machine over, care should be taken to protect oneself from injury. Firstly, ensure that the machine is completely disconnected from the mains supply, and that the inlet and outlet hoses are removed. Secondly, before attempting to lay the machine over, decide if you need any help. These machines are very heavy and a little help may prevent a slipped disc! Thirdly, before attempting to move the machine, ensure that the floor is dry. A wet floor has no grip, especially if the water is soapy.

The correct rating of fuse must be used as per the manufacturer's instructions. As a general guide, the applications for the three main ratings of fuse are listed in the *General Safety Guide chapter*. Plug wiring must be connected according to the following code to ensure safety. The colours are as follows.

LIVE – BROWN
NEUTRAL – BLUE
EARTH – GREEN/YELLOW

The author would like to point out at this time, that any references to manufacturer's names or model numbers, etc., that are used throughout this manual are for the reader's information, and reference purposes only. Whilst every precaution has been taken to ensure that all information is factual in every detail, the author cannot accept any responsibility for any errors or omissions appertaining to this manual, and shall not be responsible for any damage or injury whilst using this manual.

Regular inspection points

A regular internal inspection of your washer, may enable you to identify a part that may not be running properly, or find a perished hose before a leak occurs.

It is recommended that the following points be checked regularly.

Inspect	When	Special notes
Pump filter (if fitted)	Weekly	As per manufacturer's manual. often dependent on usage.
Valve filters (hot and cold)	6 months	If dirty, pull out with pliers and wash out.
Door seal, door glass	6 months	If seal is tacky to the touch, seal may be in need of renewal soon. Rub any sticky fluff off door glass with non-abrasive pad.
All hoses	6 months	As above. Ensure that all corrugations in all hoses are checked thoroughly.
Pump and sump hose catch pot	6 months	Check for any items that may have collected in or at these points. Remove as necessary.
Suspension	6 Months	Check suspension mounts on tub and body of machine. If slide type, see suspension section.
Motor brushes (if fitted)	6 months or yearly	Check for wear and/or sticking in slides. If below half normal length, renew.
Belt tension	6 months or yearly	Check and adjust belt tension if necessary. See Chapter 29: Main Drive Belts.
Level machine	Yearly	Check that the machine is standing firmly on the floor, and that it does not rock. Adjust by unscrewing the adjustable feet, or packing under the wheels.
Check plug and connectors	After every repair	After repair, look for poor connections in the plug and socket. Also look for any cracks or other damage. Renew as necessary.
Taps and washers	After every repair	Check taps for free movement, corrosion and/or leaks.

Chapter 9

Functional Testing

Throughout the book, reference is made to functional testing to ensure that the action of the machine is correct and installation is suitable. Use this sequence as a guide to ensuring correct operation after installation, repair or servicing. The purpose is to test where practical, all functions of the machine and plumbing installation in the most efficient manner. The test will suit most types of machines which use mechanical timers/programmers. Some slight modification may be required to suit model variations. Electronically controlled machines, i.e. non-mechanical timers, will have selectable self-test programmes similar to this sequence. See *Timers (Programme Control)* chapter.

A typical installation and functional test

1. With the machine in its correct operating position and levelled correctly, and with all panels fitted, ensure that both hot and cold taps and power supply socket are turned on.
2. Ensure the door is correctly closed and latched.
3. It is not necessary to put a wash load into the machine or detergent in the dispenser for this type of test.
4. Select a hot wash cycle (90–95 degrees). On most machines this will only energise the hot fill valve and therefore test the flow rate/pressure supplied to it. The machine should fill to low level within four minutes. if the water pressure is adequate. If the fill time is more than this period, check that the hot supply tap is fully turned on. In most instances little can be done for slow hot filling, (*see: Basics – Plumbing*) and will in general cause only minor problems such as failing to dispense powders effectively from the drawer. In severe cases either connect to cold supply with a 'Y' joint or alternatively, the powder could quite simply be sprinkled over the wash load in the drum, (only if the wash is to be started immediately), still allowing the machine to take the hot fill at its reduced rate. **Note:** Some machines can be modified internally. Instruction for this will be given in the accompanying user handbook/installation document supplied with the machine. Follow the instructions given and do not attempt alteration without the detailed instructions of the manufacturer. As with any repair, inspection or maintenance, isolate the machine thoroughly prior to removing any panels.
5. Check for drum action when machine has filled to low level. Some machines may require the timer to be advanced slightly to avoid a paused heat only cycle before drum rotation takes place. See *Timers (Programme Control)* chapter (Thermostop). Check for clockwise and counter-clockwise drum action.
6. Check that the door interlock operates and that the door will not open during this cycle.
7. Switch the machine off and move it to the special treatments (fabric conditioner) position. This will select a higher level fill via the cold valve. Some machines will possess a choice of the positions for this – one before the short or delicates spin and one before the normal or fast spin. Remember on delicate cycles the machine will stop full of water after the special treatments cycle and will only move on to the spin when instructed to. Each machine has its own way of impulsing to the spin from this 'hold' position so make yourself aware from your handbook. See also *Machine Will*

Not Empty chapter.

7a. If you choose the position prior to the normal spin, the machine will fill to its high level using the cold valve and therefore a check of the cold inlet can be made. Wait four minutes maximum for the high level to be reached. As the cold inlet pressure is usually governed by the street mains to the house the pressure is normally well above the minimum required.

8. When the high level is reached check for rotation, again clockwise and counter-clockwise.

9. As the programme of Special Treatments is short, allow the machine to impulse normally to the pump out stage. (If delicate cycle, use the normal advance mechanism). Check that the machine empties within one minute or thereabouts (verifying that the pump rate and outlet are correct).

10. Allow the machine to impulse on to the spin and through to the 'off' position. Time and spin speeds will differ depending on whether special treatments cycle or whichever spin speed was selected.

11. Check immediately after the 'off' position has been reached to see if entry to the machine is correctly inhibited by the interlock.

12. Time the delay of the interlock minimum one minute up to two minutes. Check that after such time the door can be opened correctly. Do not be impatient and force the latch mechanism or handle.

This simple sequence is likely to take 10–15 minutes.

If at any point a fault should occur, the correct action can be implemented.

These simple steps have in effect, confirmed (or otherwise) the operation of both water valves and pressure supplied to them, the pressure system for water level control, hoses and seals, outlet pump and waste, programmer (though not in depth) and spin speed. However, what this relatively simple test has not shown is whether the wash heater works or if the wash thermostat operates correctly. To confirm this, the time taken to heat up to the selected temperature should be noted, also the correct impulse from the thermostat for that particular programme setting. These two items will be tested on the next full wash cycle after the basic functional test proves satisfactory. It is therefore advisable to check both heating and correct temperature advancing on a normal wash cycle.

Chapter 10

Using a flowchart

Flowcharts are used throughout the book, and are designed to help you quickly locate the area or areas of trouble, and to show that a step-by-step approach to even the most difficult of faults, is by far the best way to ensure they are found and rectified easily.

The use of flowcharts to those with some experience of home computers will need little explanation. To those of you who will be seeing them for the first time, here is how they work.

How flowcharts work

To the uninitiated, the use of flowcharts may seem a difficult way of fault finding. This is not the case, and will be quite simple if a few small, but important points are remembered. As you will see in the examples, there are only three main types of symbols used. A rectangular box, a diamond and an elipse. With a little practise, you will become aware how invaluable this method can be in all areas of D.I.Y. work. The construction of one's own flowchart before attempting the job in hand, will be of help when the time comes to reverse the stripdown procedure, i.e., notes can be made next to the relevant boxes on the flowchart, of what was encountered at that point, i.e., number of screws, positions of wires, etc. Small points – but so vital, and so often forgotten with an unplanned approach.

The rectangular box

This is a process, i.e., in the box is an instruction. Carry it out, and rejoin the flowchart where you left it, travelling in the direction indicated by the arrows.

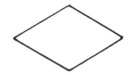

The diamond

This asks a question, i.e., if the answer to the question in the diamond is "yes", then follow the line from the point of the box, i.e., the box asks if a pipe is blocked. The junction to the left is marked *"no"* and the junction to the right is marked *"yes"*. If the pipe is blocked, follow the line to the right.

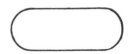

The elipse

This is a terminator. When this box is encountered, you either start a new chart or finish one. The text in the box will indicate the action.

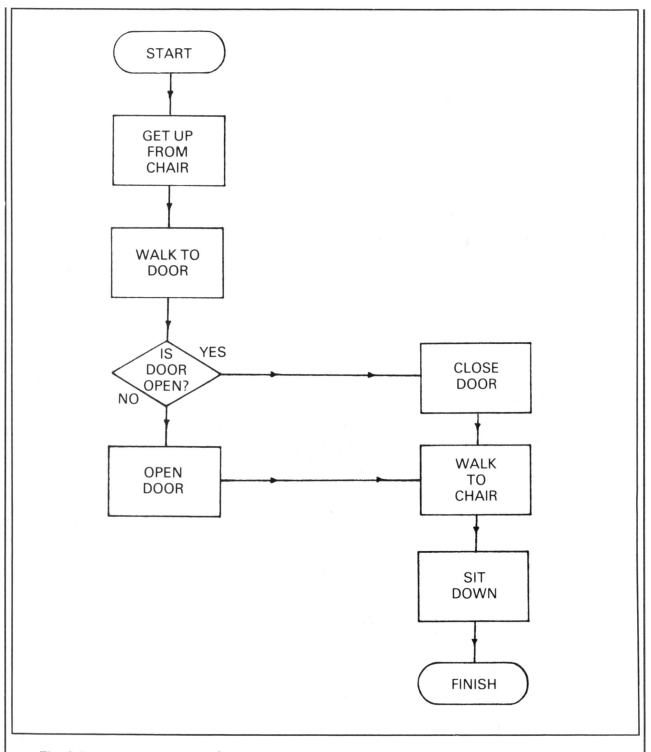

The following example flowchart illustrates the steps involved in carrying out the simple task of opening a closed door, and closing an open door. The arrows indicate the direction to the next step, so as to guide you through the logical sequence.

Chapter 11

Plugs and Sockets

Problems with electrical appliances may not always be the result of a failure of the item itself but with the electrical supply to it via the socket. A three-pin socket must have a Live supply, a Neutral return and a sound Earth path. When a plug from an appliance is inserted in the socket, a firm contact must be made at all three points. If the live or neutral pins of the plug or connection point within the socket fail to make adequate contact or are free to move, localised heating will occur within the socket.

Problem spotting

Telltale signs of this type of fault often show themselves as:
1. Burn marks around one or both entry points on the socket.
2. Plug hot to the touch after use of appliance in that socket.
3. Pungent smell from socket when appliance is in use.
4. Pitting and burn marks on and around the pins of the plug.
5. Radio interference to nearby equipment caused by internal arcing within the socket creating spurious radio emissions. These may pass along the ring main to hi-fi units, etc.
6. Intermittent or slow operation of the appliance being used.
7. Failure of the fuse in the plug. In this instance, this is not caused by a fault within the appliance but by heat being transferred through the live pin and into the fuse which fails by over-heating.

All these conditions are more likely with appliances such as washing machines, heaters and kettles, etc., which draw a high current when in use.

Why does it happen?

The reasons for such problems are various and may be caused by one or a combination·of any of those listed below:

1. Repeated use of the socket, opening up the contact points within the socket. In other words general wear and tear.
2. Poor quality socket or plug.
3. Loose pins on plug.
4. The use of a double adaptor. This can cause a poor connection purely by the weight of cables and plugs pulling the adaptor partially out of the wall socket. Worse still is allowing a number of high-current-draw appliances to be run through one socket thus causing overloading. Examples might be a fan heater and kettle or washing machine and tumble dryer. Whenever possible, avoid the use of adaptors by provision of an adequate number of sockets and do not exceed 3 kW load on any single socket.

Socket highlighting overheating. Both plug and socket will require replacing.

5. Use of a multi-point extension lead when the total load on the trailing socket can easily exceed the 3 kW load of the single socket supply.

Note: It is unwise to use a washing machine or similar items via an extension lead. Make provision for a convenient 13amp supply socket to accommodate the original length of the appliance cable.

Rectification

First, DO NOT use the socket until the problem has been rectified. If the socket is found to be showing any of the previously described faults, it must be renewed completely. If it is a single socket it may be wise to have a double socket fitted as a replacement. Numerous DIY books describe the renewal of sockets so I won't duplicate the instructions here. Suffice it to say that caution should be exercised when tackling socket renewal. When buying a replacement socket, make sure it is a good quality one as there are many of dubious quality to be found. Price is a good indicator of quality in this field.

It is advisable to renew all plugs that have been used in the faulty socket because damage may have been done to the plug. It is possible, of course, that a faulty plug damaged the socket. To continue using the old plugs could result in premature failure of your new unit.

As with sockets, plugs can be found in many styles and qualities. While some of the poorer quality plugs may prove to be reliable on low current consumption items like lamps, TV and radios, they may not be so good for washing machines and heaters, etc. Although British Standards do apply to these items, quality does vary considerably. When buying plugs and sockets, go to outlets that can give advice and that carry a good selection. This will allow

you to compare quality and build of the products. Look for the ASTA mark which proves that the design and manufacture has been approved by the Association of Short Circuit Testing Authorities. Replacement fuses should also carry this mark.

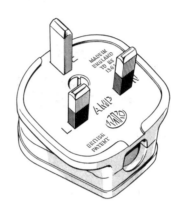

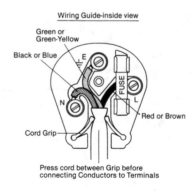

Wiring Guide-inside view

Green or Green-Yellow

Black or Blue

E

FUSE

N

L

Red or Brown

Cord Grip

Press cord between Grip before connecting Conductors to Terminals

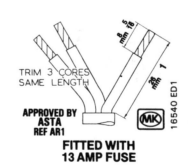

TRIM 3 CORES SAME LENGTH

16540 ED 1

APPROVED BY ASTA REF AR1

(MK)

FITTED WITH 13 AMP FUSE

Specific requirements for MK plugs.

Always look for the ASTA sign when purchasing electrical fittings.

The earth

All of the faults mentioned previously relate to the 'live' supply and neutral return on the socket, the plug or both. There is, of course, a third pin. Although it takes no active part in the operation of the appliance, it is, however, the most important connection of all. The function of the earth system is explained in 'Basics — Electrical'. Products that have three core cable must have the yellow and green earth wire securely connected to the earth pin of the plug or pin marked E.

The earth path of an appliance can be checked easily using a simple test meter (*see* Electrical Circuit Testing). Remember, a path of low resistance is required from all items within the product that are linked into the earth path via the yellow and green cable.

NOTE: The earth path of an appliance from its exposed metal parts to the earth pin of the plug should be a maximum of 1 ohm (BS3456).

Checking the socket will require the use of an earth loop test meter which needs to be operated correctly. As these meters are expensive and problems could be encountered with distribution boards fitted with an RCCD, it is advisable to have these tests done by a qualified electrical contractor. A simple plug-in tester like the one shown can be found in most good electrical shops and DIY outlets. This is most useful for checking the socket for reverse polarity. In other words, it will show whether a socket has been incorrectly wired. An incorrectly wired socket can still work and outwardly give no sign of any problem. This type of fault is dangerous and not uncommon. The plug-in tester also indicates if an earth path is present. However, the quality of the earth in the socket is not shown. That is to say, it may have a very high resistance but would still allow the neon of the tester to light. If the earth resistance is high, remember this may result in a failure to blow the fuse which may cause overheating at the high resistance point or allow a flow of electricity through anything or anyone else that can give a better route to earth.

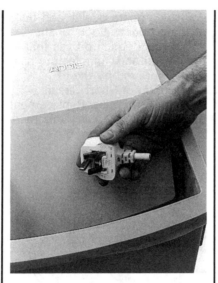

Make sure a moulded plug removed from an appliance cannot be inadvertently plugged in. Remove the fuse and bend the pins.

Typical plug in socket tester.

Typical resilient plugs which can stand up to rugged use without cracking.

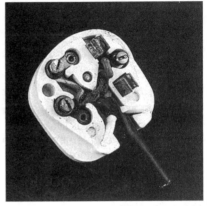

Internal view of severe burnout caused by poor connection to terminal. A new plug is required and the cable cut back to sound wire or renewed.

Incorrectly fitted plug. Wiring bunched and not trimmed to right lengths. Ensure all plugs are fitted correctly.

Typical moulded plug.

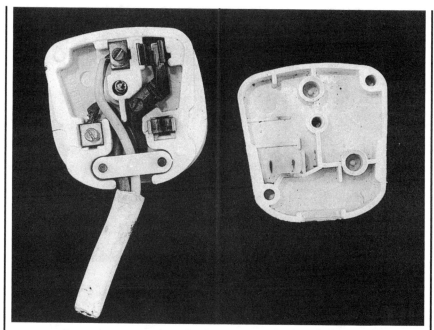

Wiring not cut to correct length. As a result the cord grip is fixed across inner wires, not outer sheath.

Plug fitting

The fitting of a plug is often believed to be a straight-forward task that needs little or no explanation. On the contrary, this is an area where many problems are to be found and dangers encountered if the fitting is not done correctly. Do not neglect this most important item.

The following text and photo sequences deal specifically with modern 13A flat-pin plugs. If your property has round-pin plugs and sockets, the indication is that the house wiring may be old and it would be wise to have it checked thoroughly by an expert.

When wiring a plug, it is good practice to leave the earth wire (yellow/green) longer than is necessary merely for connection to the earth terminal to be accomplished. The extra length is taken up in a slight loop shape within the plug. Doing this means that, should the appliance flex be pulled hard accidentally and the plug's cable grip fail to hold, the live and neutral wires will detach from the terminal first, leaving the earth loop intact

Conductor wire protruding from plug pins.

Note: All of the above photographs are used to illustrate the lack of attention to safety to this small but vital component. Always fit plugs correctly and safely. To give further assistance, a step-by-step photo guide for the two types of plug is given overleaf.

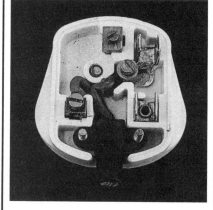

Wiring incorrectly bunched into plug to allow cord grip to hold outer sheath.

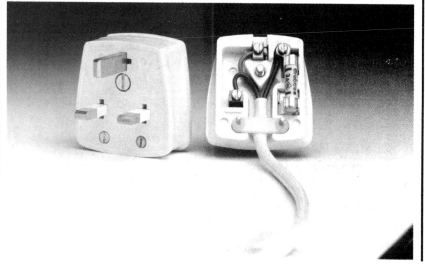

High quality three-pin plug ideal for home appliances.

to provide continued safety cover. The photo of the pillar-type plug shows how the extra little bit of earth wire is contained inside the plug. The post and nut plug shown does not allow for this and the manufacturer recommends that all wires to be cut to the same length (as shown).

Wiring a plug – pillar type.

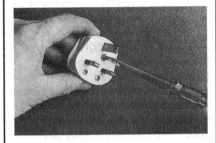

1. Remove the screw that holds the plug top/cover in position, taking care not to lose it.

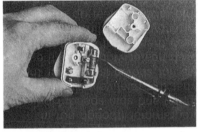

2. Ease the fuse from position (if using a screwdriver, take care not to damage it).

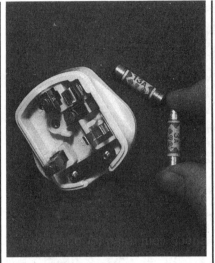

3. Check that the fuse supplied with the plug is of the correct rating for the appliance. Many plugs are supplied with 13 amp fuse already fitted, but do not be tempted to use it unless it is right. In this instance a 3 amp fuse was required.

4. Carefully remove the outer cable sheath to expose the inner wires. If damage should occur to the inner wires in the process, cut back and start again.

5. Offer the wiring to the plug base with the outer sheath in its correct position resting in the cord clamp area. Next, cut the inner cables to suit, allowing ½ in (13mm) past the fixing point. Don't forget to allow a little extra on the earth cable to form a slight loop.

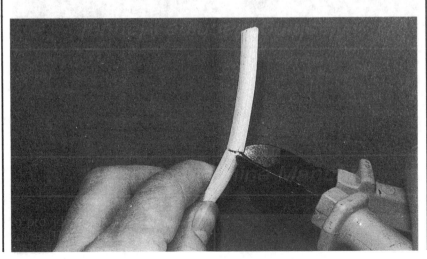

6. Carefully remove ¼ in (6mm) of insulation from the end of each wire. This must be done with care to avoid damaging or cutting any strands of the conductor.

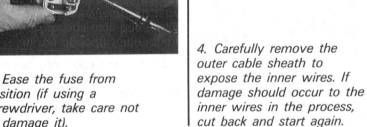

7. Twist the strands of each wire securely together. Make sure there are no loose strands.

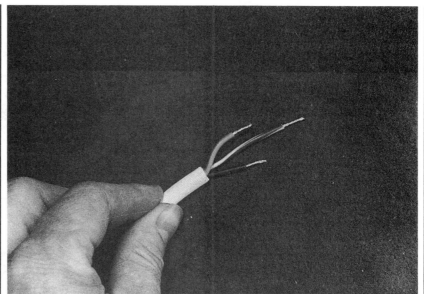

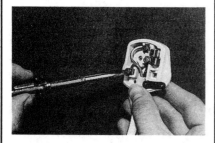

8. Fit each wire into its correct pillar and tighten each screw ensuring that it grips the conductor firmly (with thin wires it will help if they are folded over on themselves first). Make sure the wire fits up to the insulation shoulder and no wires or strands protrude from the pillar.

9. Fit the cord clamp over the outer sheath and screw it firmly into position while being careful not to strip the threads of the plastic grip.

10. Before refitting the top/cover, double check all fixings. Ensure the wiring is seated and routed neatly and is not under stress or bunched. Fit the correct rated fuse, making sure that it is firmly and securely positioned.

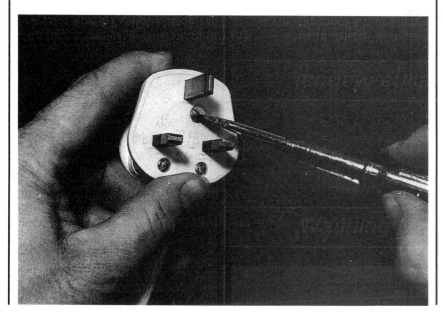

11. With top/cover refitted tighten the securing screw.

Wiring a plug – post and nut type

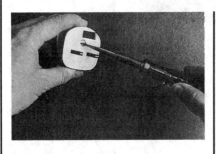

1. Remove the screw that holds plug top/cover in position.

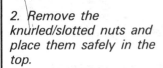

2. Remove the knurled/slotted nuts and place them safely in the top.

3. With the plug top/cover removed, the fuse can be eased from its position. If using a screwdriver, take care not to damage the fuse.

5. Carefully remove $1\frac{1}{4}$ in (32mm) of the cable sheath to expose the inner wires. If damage should occur to the inner wires in the process, cut back and start again.

7. Twist the strands of each wire securely together. Make sure there are no loose strands.

4. Check that the fuse supplied with the plug is of the correct rating for the appliance. Many plugs are supplied with 13 amp fuse already fitted but do not be tempted to use it unless it is right. In this instance a 13 amp fuse was required.

6. Now remove $\frac{9}{16}$ in (15mm) of insulation from the end of each wire. This must be done with care to avoid damaging or cutting any strands of the conductor.

8. The prepared cable can now be inserted into the cord grip ensuring only the outer sheath of the cable is gripped.

9. Fit each conductor (wire) to its correct terminal. Make sure each is fitted in a clockwise direction otherwise it will be pushed out as the nut is tightened. Ensure only the conductor is gripped and not the outer insulation.

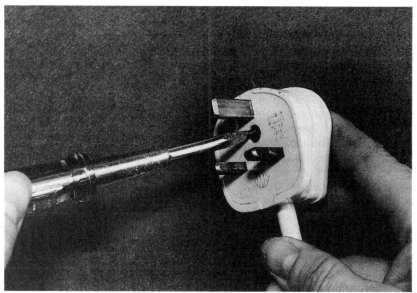

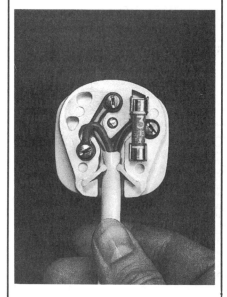

10. Securely tighten all three nuts. Ensure that the wire fits up to the insulation shoulder and no wires or strands protrude from the terminal. Before refitting the top/cover, double-check all fixings. Ensure the wiring is seated and routed neatly and is not under stress or bunched. Fit the correct rated fuse, making sure that it is firmly and securely positioned.

11. With top/cover refitted tighten the securing screw. This type has a captive screw with a shockproof washer to prevent it working loose during use.

Moulded plugs

Some appliances may be supplied with one-piece moulded 13 amp plugs fitted to the mains cable. If for any reason this type of plug has to be removed (e.g. to allow the cable to be slotted through a hole in a work surface, or due to damage), because of its moulded construction, it is not possible to take it off in the normal way. The plug has to be cut off with suitable wire cutters and a new plug fitted correctly as shown.

Warning: Any moulded plug removed in this way must be disposed of immediately. It is wise to remove the fuse and to bend the pins of the plug as soon as it is removed to make sure that it cannot be inadvertently plugged into a socket. Do not leave it lying about or dispose of it where children can find it and plug it in.

Do's and Don'ts

DO ensure the cable insulation is removed carefully. Use of the correct wire strippers is recommended.

DO make sure that connections are the right way around.

DO ensure that wires are trimmed to suit plug fixing points and no bunching is present. See poorly fitted plugs illustrations.

DO make sure that all connections are tight and no strands of wire are left protruding from terminals. To prevent this, twist the strands together as shown, prior to fitting.

DO make sure that the cord grip is fitted correctly around the outer insulation only.

DO ensure correct rating of fuse is used to suit appliance.

DO ensure the plug top/cover fits tightly and securely with no cracks or damage present.

DO NOT damage the inner core of wires when removing the outer or inner insulation. If you do, cut back and start again.

DO NOT fit tinned ends of cables into plugs. Some manufacturers tin (dip in solder) the end of the exposed inner conductors. The tinned/soldered end, if fitted to the plug, will work loose and cause problems associated with loose connections. Although tight when fitted, constant pressure over a long period will compress the soft solder resulting in a loose joint. A second problem associated with tinned conductors is the excessive length of exposed inner wire which the manufacturer usually provides. This can protrude below the cord clamp bunch within the plug to allow the cord clamp to clamp the outer insulation only. Both of these practices are dangerous and must be avoided. Always cut cable lengths to suit the plug. If this poor method of fitting is found on an appliance it must be corrected immediately.

DO NOT allow strands of wire to protrude from any fixing points.

DO NOT fit incorrect fuse ratings. Always match fuses to appliances and observe the manufacturer's instructions.

DO NOT re-use overheated or damaged plugs.

DO NOT by-pass the internal fuse.

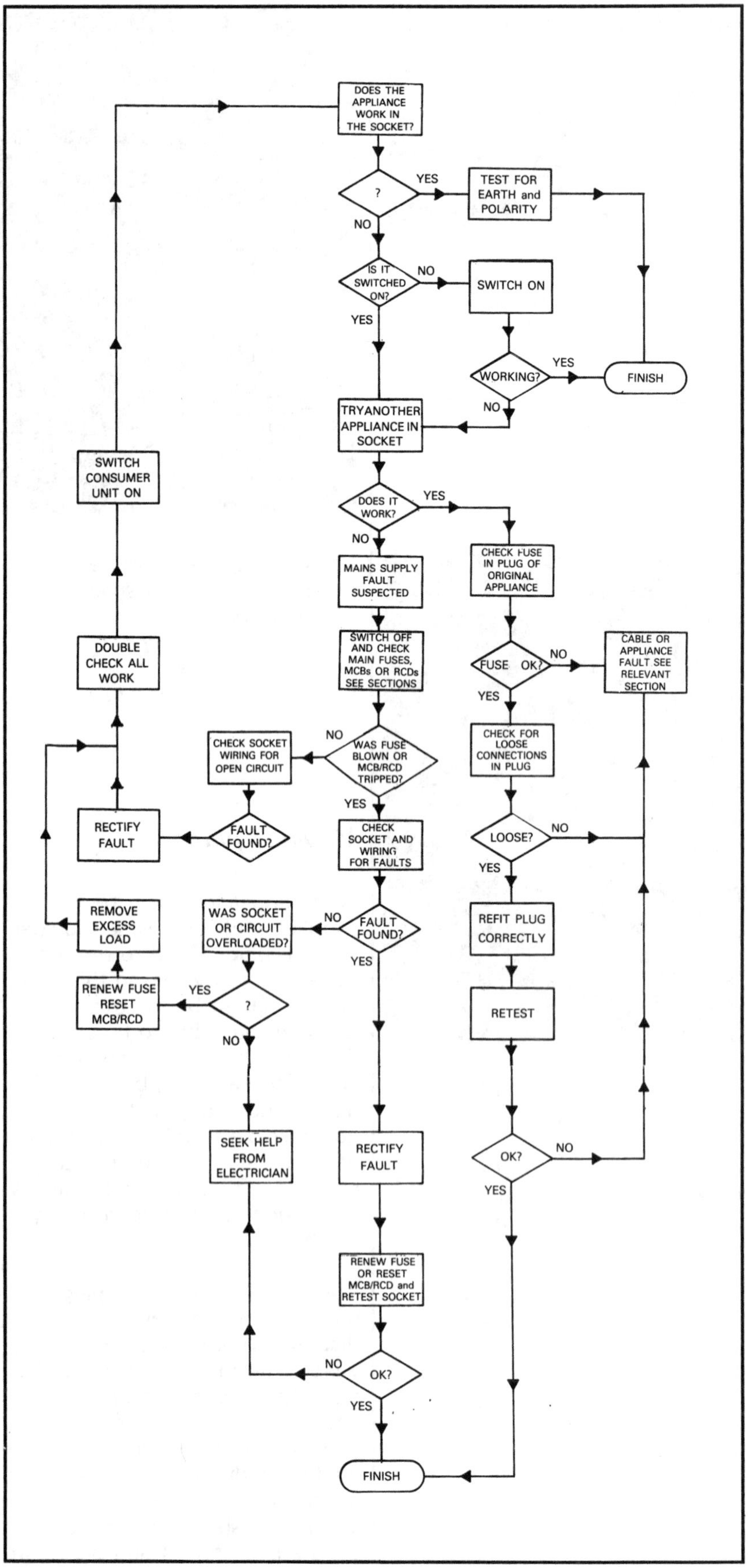

*PLUGS
AND SOCKETS
FLOWCHART*

Chapter 12

Determining the Fault

Throught the manual, flowcharts are used to aid the fault finding process. The location of faults will become much easier as you become more conversant with your machine, i.e., through regular servicing of your machine before faults have arisen.

Selecting the correct flowchart for the job will be made easier if it is remembered that faults fall into three main categories, mechanical, electrical and chemical.

Mechanical faults will normally become apparent by a change in the usual operational noise level of the machine, for instance a faulty suspension may cause a banging or bumping noise. A broken or slipping belt (incorrect tension) may give rise to excessive spin noise or little or no drum rotation. This may also indicate a drum or motor bearing fault.

Electrical faults fall into two major categories:
Impulse path faults A fault is classed as an impulse fault when an internal, pre-determined instruction has failed, i.e. thermostat does not close or open at the required temperature, or the timer fails to move on after a given time

sequence. This constitutes an impulse path fault. Simply, this is the failure of the machine to move correctly through its selected programme. An instance of this type of fault is explained.

The timer supplies power to the heater, but due to a fault in the thermostat circuit, the timer

Shown is a simplified flowchart of the operation described.

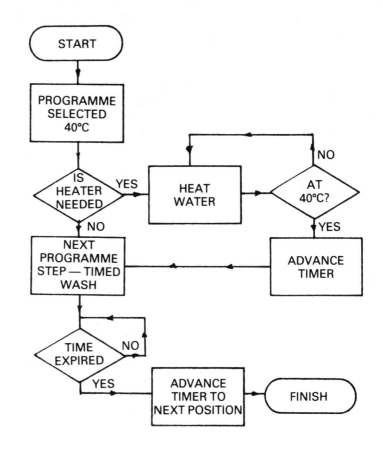

37

is not supplied with the information that the correct temperature has been reached. Because of this the timer does not move on, but remains on the heat position and exceeds the selected temperature. It should be noted that there is no fault in the timer, just in one of its impulse paths. A similar fault would arise even if the thermostat circuit was satisfactory, the thermostat closed at the correct temperature, but the timer failed to move on after the correct time had elapsed. This would be a fault of the timer's internal impulse path via its timing mechanism, and would constitute a component fault, i.e., timer coil, thermostop or complete timer unit. See *Timers (Programme Control)*.

Component faults A fault is classed as a component fault when a complete unit has failed. If the pump, heater, motor, etc., should fail, the fault is said to be a component fault.

Chemical faults These are normally associated with the powder being used and will cover such problems as poor washing, scaling problems, blocking, etc. A comprehensive guide to washing problems and useful hints will be found at the rear of this manual, in the chapter *Common Causes of Poor Washing Results*.

Fault finding reference guide

Appropriate chapter headings are listed below the fault

Machine will not work at all
Basics chapters
Locating a fault
Door switches (interlocks)

Machine leaks
Emergency procedures
Locating a fault
Leaks, fault finding
Water level control
Pumps
Motor
Water inlet valves
Suspension

Machine will not empty
Emergency procedures
Locating a fault
Pumps
Basic plumbing
Wiring harness faults

Machine will not fill/take powder
Basics
Locating a fault
Water inlet valves

Machine does not wash clean
Locating a fault
Main drive belt (tension)
Common causes of poor wash results
Basic plumbing
Pumps

Machine is noisy
Noise faults
　　Bearings
　　Motor
Suspension

Machine washes but no spin
Locating a fault
Door switches (interlocks)
Pumps
　　Motor
　　Motor – speed control

Machine will not turn drum
Main drive belt
　　Motor
　　Motor – speed control
Door switches (interlocks)

Machine spins on all positions
Locating a fault
Motors – module control
　　Motor
Timer – (programme control)

Machine won't move through programme
Basic plumbing
Temperature control (thermostat)
Heater
Water inlet valve
Timers (programme control)

Machine sticks through programme
Locating a fault
Basic plumbing
Pump
Timers (programme control)
Water inlet valve

Machine blows fuses
Emergency procedures
General safety guide
Basics — Electrical
Low insulation

The lists below the main fault headings indicate the sequence with which they should be examined.

Chapter 13

Noise faults

Noise can be one of the first signs that something is going wrong with your washing machine. Noise faults are easily ignored, and over a length of time can be accepted as the norm, and because of this it is important that noise faults be examined immediately.

As with other faults, noise faults become easier to locate the more conversant that you become with your machine.

Noises and their most common locations

A loud grating or rumbling noise would indicate a main drum bearing fault. See *Bearings and bearing replacement* chapter.

A loud high pitched noise would indicate a main motor bearing or pump bearing fault. See motors and pumps chapters.

A noise just before and after spin, would indicate wear or water penetration of the suspension mounts. See *Suspension* chapter.

A squeaking noise mainly during the wash cycle, would indicate a poorly adjusted drive belt. Instructions on how to adjust the drive belt appear in the *Main drive belts* chapter.

A specific fault can be found on machines with cast aluminium pulleys. If a crack or break develops in one leg/spoke of the pulley, a noise very similar to that of main bearing failure can be heard. Check such pulleys closely for this type of defect and also for tight fit on shaft of drum, i.e., should not be loose fit. See *Bearings* chapter. This type of fault may be apparent on both wash or spin cycles alike.

Coin damage

Coins and other metal items are easily trapped in the machine, and can cause a great deal of damage. These can become trapped between the inner drum

Typical coin damage to a drum. This kind of fault can be easily avoided by careful checking of pockets, etc., prior to loading the washer. If this type of damage has been caused, the only cure is to carry out a complete drum renewal.

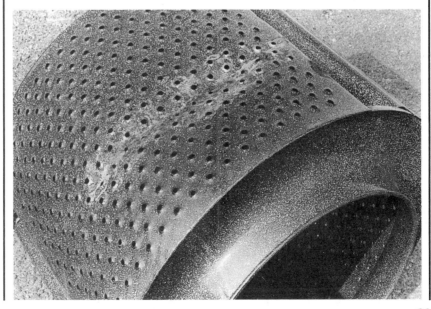

and outer tub, and should be removed before damage to the drum occurs.

Coin damage can be identified by small bumps on the inner drum or a rattling noise when spinning. On enamel drums, this may be accompanied by small flakes of enamel in the wash load. It is not uncommon on machines with stainless steel drums for the drum to be torn open by coin damage. Take care when checking the drum interior for this kind of damage as the torn metal edges can be extremely sharp. In such instances the inner drum will need to be renewed as a repair is not possible. Small pips of plastic found in the wash load may indicate the presence of a coin or similar item trapped between the inner and outer tub.

Where there is no damage to the drum, it may be possible to avoid a full stripdown/removal by removing the coin from the drum/tub gap by removing the heater, see: *Heater* chapter. The item can either be removed via this opening, or manoeuvred into the sump hose, where it can be extracted easily. To refit the heater, see *The Heater* chapter. **Note**: Any large items such as bra wires, keys, etc., can be removed via the heater opening avoiding the sharp 90 degree angle into the sump hose. All such problems could of course be avoided by first removing all items from pockets, etc., before washing. This simple action can save a lot of time and money in the long run.

Typical damage caused by coin damage to an outer tub.
Although this does not seem as bad as the damage to the previous drum photograph, the chips on the enamel will cause corrosion.

To cure this type of damage, treat the affected areas with an anti-corrosion compound. This is readily available in motorists' shops and is generally used for minor car bodywork repairs.

When applying the above compound, please ensure that the manufacturer's instructions are followed carefully, and that the compound does not come into contact with rubber hoses or seals, etc. Always use this type of substance in a well ventilated area.

Stainless steel or plastic tubs are not generally affected by this type of damage, although regular inspection is important.

Do not apply anti-corrosion compound to plastic tubs.

Chapter 14

Leaks fault finding

This fault is by far the one that causes the most mess and inconvenience. A small leak/weep can damage other parts of the machine as well as floorboards, carpets and cupboards over many months, whilst appearing to function normally. Above all, the safety factor of a mains powered machine with a water leak should be considered. If a machine has a leak, regardless of how small, it must be checked out and cured. A very small and inexpensive seal may be the cause of the leak that is possibly damaging the main motor. The hoses should have been inspected regularly, as stated in the section: *Regular inspection points*.

With the above in mind, the flowchart can be followed. At first it may seem obvious where the leak is coming from, but it would still be wise to follow the flowchart through.

Box 1:

The smallest of holes in the door boot (door seal) can be the cause of the biggest leaks. The condition of the seal should also be checked and replaced if any holes are found or if it feels sticky or tacky to the touch. The seal between the door glass and the seal should be a good one, with no scaling or fluff adhering to the door glass. If this is the case, it can be easily removed by rubbing gently with a non-abrasive scouring pad. Details of door seal replacement can be found in the *Door seal* chapter.

Box 2:

The clamp band that secures the door seal to the washer should be checked for tightness. Details of different types of clamp bands can be found in the *Door seal* chapter.

Box 3:

The dispenser hose is located at the base of the soap dispenser, and forms the connection with the tub. Again, thorough inspection of this hose is advised, as all of the water that the machine uses passes through this hose, and can therefore lead to some quite large leaks. This hose is usually of a grommet type fitting, and should be checked for tightness, i.e., it should not rotate. A sign of a bad fit is scaling/powder marks running down the outer tub at the fitting point. If the hose feels sticky or tacky to the touch, it should be replaced. **Note:** If this hose has leaked, the water would have contained detergent. If the water has come into contact with the suspension legs it may cause a loud squeaking/grinding noise just before and after the spin. (This fault is more pronounced on Hoover Automatics). This is because the suspension works its hardest at this time. Please refer to the *Suspension* chapter.

If your type of washer has a hose connected between the outer rub and the rear of the machine, this is called an air vent tube. This in itself cannot leak as no water passes through it, although it may be used if the machine overfoamed, overfilled or was spun whilst still full of water. The hose is of the grommet fitting type, and should be checked for perishing as before. Most modern machines use the soap dispenser as the air vent as well as the water inlet, thus eliminating an extra grommet fitting hose in manufacture.

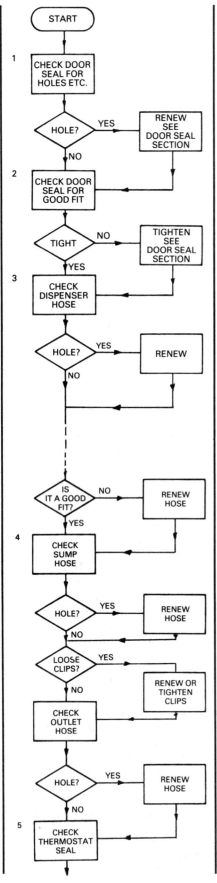

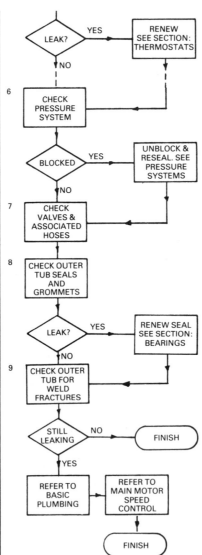

should be checked for tightness as explained in the pumps section. If the machine is of the type with a filter, all hoses to and from the filter housing and the filter seal should be checked for defects. At this point it would be advisable to thoroughly check the pump as detailed in the *Pumps* chapter.

Box 5:

The thermostat and heater seal are both generally located on the back half or underside of the outer tub, depending on the make and model of the machine. An exception to this rule is the Hotpoint front loader, where the thermostat, heater and pressure vessel are located on the front of the outer tub, directly below the door seal. Access to these components is gained by the removal of the front panel of the machine. Details of this are to be found in the *Door seals* chapter.

If the heater seal is found to be leaking, this can sometimes be stopped by tightening the centre nut. This increases the width of the rubber seal by squashing it 'vice like'. If the leak persists at this point, the heater will have to be changed completely, as the seal is not available as a separate item.

Box 6:

The connections between the pressure switches and the tub should be checked now, as detailed in the *Pressure system* chapter.

Box 7:

The hoses and clips on the inlet valves should now be checked in conjunction with *Water inlet valves* chapter. On earlier valves there is a slight chance that the top of the valve can split. This is often shown by a small brown rust patch on the top of the valve.

Box 4:

The sump hose is the flexible hose located at the bottom of the machine. Depending on the make and model of your appliance, this will be in one of two configurations:
(a) Linking the pump and the tub.
(b) Linking the filter and tub, with a separate hose linking the filter and pump, thus creating a trap for any foreign bodies to prevent them reaching the pump.

Again this should be checked for perishing and replaced if found to be tacky or sticky. The grommet fittings should also be checked, as explained in Box 3, and the clips

Box 8:

The tub seal and grommets are to be checked now. This means the seal or seals that fit between the separate parts of the main tub assembly. In addition to these seals, small rubber grommets may be found. These will have been fitted to block 'machine holes' that are used in the manufacture of the machine. If these come out or leak, they should be replaced or have sealant applied to them. If the large tub seals leak they should also be renewed. This type of repair is described in the *Drum bearing* chapter.

Box 9:

Any corrosion or flaking of the enamel covering of the outer tub can be treated with a good brand of rust inhibitor, taking care that it does not come into contact with any of the internal rubber hoses, etc., and is used in conjunction with the manufacturer's instructions. Places to note, are where the brackets for the motor and the suspension are welding onto the outer tub. These are stress points where the enamel may crack and flake, and rust will inevitably form. By the time a leak has started at these points, it is too late to save the outer tub, and it must be renewed completely if a lasting repair is to be made. *It is felt that the occurrence of tub renewal on today's modern automatics, is very rare. Therefore, the need for a lengthy section in this book would be unnecessary. Also, the cost of such items and all the relevant seals and parts necessary to complete such a repair would not be cost effective.*
    If the machine still leaks after these checks, please refer to the *Basic plumbing* and *Motors* chapters.

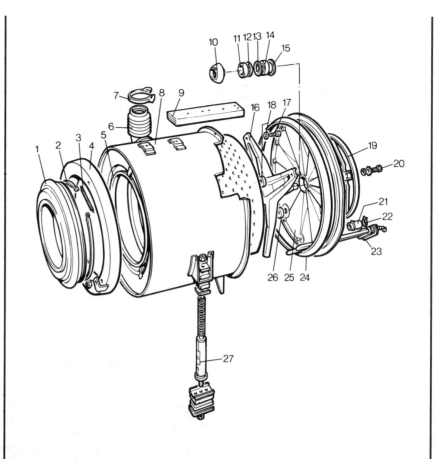

Exploded view of typical drum assembly.

1 Door seal (door boot).
2 Clamp band.
3 Spring fastening for clamp band (could be bolt or rubber garter type).
4 Front tub weight size and position may vary.
5 Tub lip for door seal to locate onto.
6 Dispenser hose.
7 Dispenser hose clip.
8 Outer tub. Position of tub weights vary.
9 Top tub weights. Locations vary.
10 Carbon face seal for main bearing.
11 Front drum bearings. (ball bearing type).
12 Front bearing spacer.
13 Rear bearing spacer.
14 Rear bearing (ball bearing type).
15 Securing clip (spring type).
16 Drum spider. (detachable version).
17 Spider fixing bolt.
18 Spider washer and spacer.
19 Drum pulley.
20 Drum pulley fixing bolt and locking tab.
21 Pressure vessel hose.
22 Pressure vessel hose clip (spring corbin clips).
23 Heater.
24 Rear tub seal. (back half seal).
25 Backhalf casting.
26 Thermostat grommet.
27 Suspension unit. (spring damper type).

Chapter 15

Machine will not empty

Of all the faults reported, this must be one of the most common. Often this fault and the 'leak' fault are one of the same. The reason for this being that on many machines there is no 'spin inhibit system'. This is especially true of older machines, or machines that are produced abroad. If there is no spin inhibit system, it means that if for any reason the machine cannot empty, it will still try to spin. The consequence of this action, is that the increased drum speed pressurises the inner tub, causing leaks from soap dispensers, air vent hoses and door seals. Thus one fault can cause several problems. On most later machines and most of the machines currently produced in Britain, the level switch inhibits (stops) the machine *before* the spin if a level of water is detected. This means that if there is water in the machine, the pressure causes the switch to switch to the *off* position, therefore not allowing the machine to spin. For a more detailed description of the pressure switch, please refer to the *Water level control* chapter.

The 'not emptying' fault can fall into three main categories: blockage, mechanical fault or

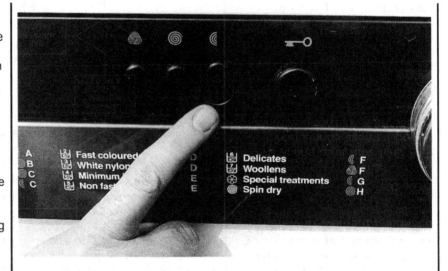

Check the position of the half spin or no spin button. This may simply (and correctly) be causing a 'spin inhibit' or 'rinse hold' facility to operate.

electrical fault.
Please refer to the following flowchart.

Box 1:

Follow the emergency procedure for removing the water already trapped inside the machine.

Box 2:

Check the outlet and sump hoses, as well as the outlet filter (if fitted). If a blockage or a kink has been found, remove it and refit the pipe(s) and filter.

Box 3:

The pump is located at the machine end of the outlet hose, and junction of the sump hose. The small chamber should be checked for blockages, the impeller should be checked for free rotation, and that it hasn't come adrift from its mounting to the pump motor shaft. If the impeller is found to be adrift from the shaft, this would give rise to no water being pumped, although the motor itself would run. A quick way to check the connection of the shaft and impeller would be to hold the shaft whilst trying to turn the impeller. If all is well they should only turn in unison. Remember to turn anti-clockwise, or the impeller will unscrew from the shaft. If a fault is found at this point, refer to the *Pumps* chapter.

Box 3A:

If no blockage is found in the section above, and the bearings are not suspected, the stator continuity of the pump windings must be checked. Please refer to the *Using a meter* chapter.

Box 4:

At this point, the outlet hose should be checked again. An internal blockage such as a coin or button can act as a type of valve, and be very difficult to see. The best method of checking this is to connect the hose of a standard tap, observing the flow of water.

Box 5:

The final step is to check the wiring harness connection. Please refer to *Wiring harness faults*.

MACHINE WILL NOT EMPTY FLOWCHART

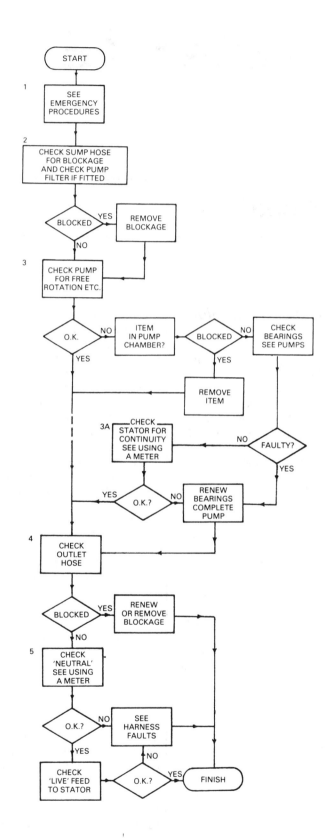

Chapter 16

Door seals

Door seal fitting – helpful hints

There are many types of door seal available, depending on make, model and the age of your machine. The removal and fitting of three typical door seals is shown. The models used in the examples are Hoover, Bendix and Hotpoint machines respectively.
The basic techniques are similar for all machines.

The door seal bridges the gap between the outer tub and the shell of the machine. This provides access to the inner drum via the door opening for loading the machine whilst also creating a watertight seal. The seal should be renewed if found to be perished or holed at any point, paying attention to the folds and mouldings of the door seal.

There are three ways that a door seal is secured to the outer tub, all very similar in concept. On the outer tub there is a formed lip. When the rubber seal is located onto this lip, it is then held in position by a large clamp band, and pressure exerted by the band to create a water-tight seal. There are several versions of clamp bands used in today's

machines. Four of the most common are described below. The majority of machines will have one or a combination of those listed whereas the others may have a variation of one of those described. Use this list to help identify the type used in your machine.

1. A simple metal band secured by a bolt, which when tightened reduces the diameter of the band.
2. As (1), but the open ends of the band are secured by a spring.
3. This method is best described as a large rubber band or spring joined together to form an expanding ring. Both types are called garter rings. When fitted correctly, the ring rests in a recess in the door seal, which in turn rests in the recess of the tub lip, therefore creating the watertight seal. Unlike the previous two methods, this band cannot be slackened by the loosening of a bolt or spring, and is best removed by prising the garter ring from its position in the seal recess by using a flat-bladed screwdriver to lift it over the lip. The best way to refit a rubber or spring garter ring is to locate the bottom of the ring in

the recess of the fitted door seal slowly working the ring inside the recess in an upward direction with both hands meeting at the top. This can be likened to fitting a tyre onto a bicycle wheel after mending a puncture.
4. A slightly unusual fastening may be encountered where both ends of a wire band are joined by a small metal plate. The ends of the wire band are linked into two holes in the metal plate. The plate has a larger hole/slot in it and if a small screwdriver is inserted into this slot and forms a tight fit, when turned, a 'cam' action occurs which reduces or increases the overall circumference. Only a small movement is required, approximately a quarter turn between open and closed. When closed correctly, the plate will lock into position. Access to the plate can be gained through the door latch hole after first removing the two interlock fixing screws. This type of fixing is mainly found on machines in the Colston/Ariston range. The reason for this type of clamp band is that access to the more usual clamp band would be impossible due to a close front fitting circular concrete tub weight which surrounds the door

seal tub lip. **Note**: To aid the fitting of a door seal, a little washing-up liquid may be applied to the tub lip or the door seal tub lip moulding. (NOT the front shell lip.) This will allow the rubber to slip more easily into position on the metal or plastic lip of the outer tub.

The fitting of the door seal to the shell of the machine is similar to the tub lip system in that three major variations are found: a) The most straightforward seal simply grips the shell lip with no other added support other than the elasticity of the door seal itself on early machines. For safety reasons modern machines now use various methods of secondary fixing to prevent the door seal being easily removed or dislodged from the shell lip. It is essential that such fixings are replaced if they have once been removed for any reason. b) This type also uses the shell lip, with the aid of a clamp band. A recess is formed on the outer edge of the seal for a clamp band or clamp wire to be inserted. This ensures a firm grip on the shell lip. As with the inner tub lip, many variations can be found, see photos. c) The third method involves a plastic flange that is screwed onto the outside of the shell. The screws that hold this flange pass through a recess in the outer front lip of the door seal therefore securing it firmly to the front panel. Variations on both of the later clamps can be found on modern machines. They are fitted as a safety measure to restrict access to the inner of the machine. It is essential that any such fixing is replaced correctly if it has had to be removed for any reason. Before removing the old door seal a simple examination of the old seal and a note of its correct positioning will aid the subsequent repair and renewal as the new seal will need to fit in exactly the same position. Some door seals have a definite top and bottom, or pre-shaped

sections for door hinges or catches, etc., and will fit no other way. Remember, it is easier to line up the seal before fitting rather than trying to adjust the seal when the clamp bands have been fitted.

Note: Some machines have one or more of their tub weights mounted on the front section of the outer tub, encircling the door seal and tub clamp fitting, leaving little or no access to the clamp band or tub lip. However, do not remove the front tub weight to aid door seal fitting as it is not necessary for most machines, e.g. Creda, Zanussi, Ariston and Bendix, etc., even though some have front tub weights surrounding the tub clamp bands. The Zanussi and Creda seals can be changed through the door opening in the front panel of the machine, without removing the top at all. (Having said this, removing the top of the machine will provide more light. Remove if necessary.)

Candy outer tub showing the tub weights in place around the front of the tub. The seal can be renewed with the weight in position. Bendix, Philco and Zanussi have weights completely surrounding the seal. The seal can still be renewed with these weights in position. Some machines do not have the large concrete weight around the front of the tub, thus allowing good access to the door seal clamp band. Hotpoint, Hoover and late Servis machines have this style of tub. (The tub shown has been removed for the purpose of the photograph – the door seals are fitted with the tub inside the machine).

The following photographic sequences show the removal and refitting of various types of door seal.

The second sequence of pictures shows the removal of a door seal from a Bendix machine. Refitting is a reversal of the removal process.

Removal of typical door seal (Hoover)

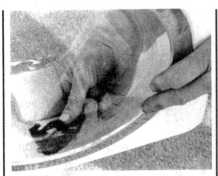

1. Check door glass inner for scale deposit ridge and clean of with non-abrasive pad.

2. Grasp door seal firmly and pull downwards to free from shell lip. Some machines may have clamp band on front lip. Remove this first.

3. When freed from lip, continue pulling in a downward direction.

4. Free complete door seal from front lip and allow seal to rest on inner side of front panel.

5. With top removed, free the top support springs or tie, and lean outer tub unit back as far as possible.

6. With position of clamp band and bolt in view proceed to remove band. Free seal from the clip as shown above.

7. New door seal of type to be fitted to the machine shown.

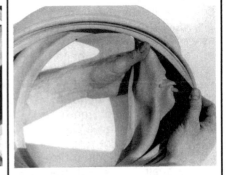

8. View showing inner lip moulding and ridge. the ridge is fitted at the 9 o'clock position when viewed from the front of the machine.

9. Cutaway view of a typical door seal to show intricate moulding and positioning of tub and shell lips of the seal.

Removal of a Bendix door seal

1. Remove the plastic flange around the door seal front.

4. Picture showing the orientation of the band inside the machine. Must be re-fitted in the same position.

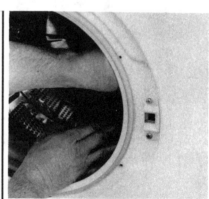

2. Remove the door seal from the front lip.

5. Slacken off tub clamp band bolt and remove old door seal.

3. Showing the position of the clamp band with the top of the machine removed.

6. View showing the tub lip and weight block gap. (Clean off any scale and/or deposit on the tub lip before fitting the new seal).

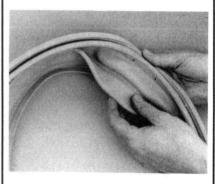

7. New door seal checked prior to fitting and smeared with a little washing up liquid to help slide it into position. (Inner lip only).

8. Ensure that the three drain holes on the door seal are fitted at the bottom of the tub lip.

Removal of a Hotpoint front loader door seal

1. Remove outer plastic surround screws, and top and bottom section.

2. Pull seal to release from shell lip, hinge and catch.

3. Unscrew the timer knob centre and remove the timer knob. Also remove the two front facia fixing screws found behind the timer knob.

4. Pull out the soap dispenser draw completely and remove the front facia fixing screws.

5. With front facia removed, remove the screws securing the front panel of the machine.

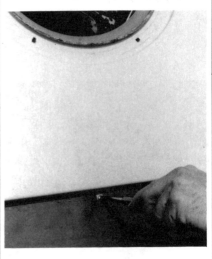

6. Four hexagonal headed screws secure the front panel under the bottom edge. (On later machines, three Philips headed screws will be found).

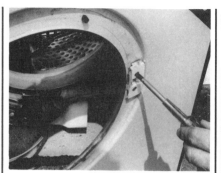

7. Remove door switch assembly and pressure switch bracket.

8. With front panel removed, the clamp band can easily be removed.

9. Note the position of hinge and catch mouldings. The door seal can then be pulled free from the tub lip.

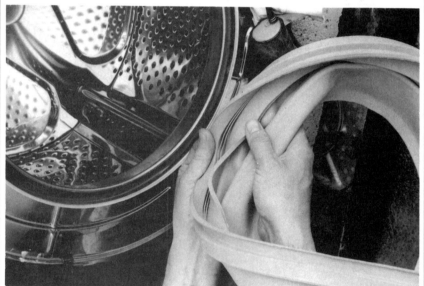

10. When fitting a new seal to the tub lip, the tub gap can be adjusted slightly. (Note: the inner lip of the door seal is ribbed).

11. When the new seal is fitted in this position, check that the inner drum rotates without fouling the door seal inner. Adjust if necessary to obtain the smallest gap possible before refitting.

12. With new door seal in this position it is wise to check that all of the leads, hoses and pressure vessel are correct before refitting the front panel.

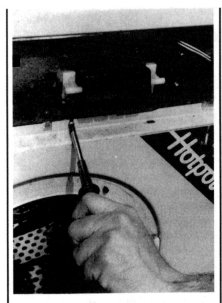

13. Refit front panel, door catch and all front panel fixings.

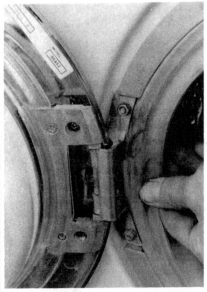

15. Lubricate the hinge and catch points with a little washing up liquid, and ease into position.

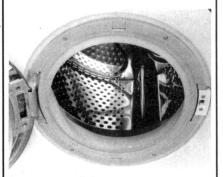

17. When fitted, the new seal should not have undue kinks or twists. It is essential that this is correctly fitted.

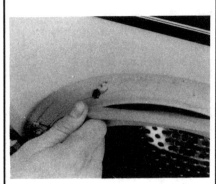

14. With front panel secured, fit the door seal to the front panel lip.

16. Refit plastic surround and ensure that the ends locate correctly. The plastic pips can be moved to aid fitting. The machine is now ready for the functional test.

Chapter 17

Water inlet valves

Inlet valve fault finding

In this section we deal with several of the most common reported faults: not taking powder, not filling at all, not filling in certain parts of the programme. Please refer to the flowchart found later in this chapter.

Many configurations of water valve can be found from single hot or cold to much larger units consisting of three or more individually operated valves grouped together to control the flow to several outlets from one inlet. All inlet point threads are the same size, but outlet hose connections from the valve may differ. A wide variety of fixing brackets are also used, outlet angles can be in-line (classed as 180 degree valves) or angled downwards (classed as 90 degree valves). Operation of the electro-mechanical action follows and covers the general operation of all such valves.

A solenoid coil of some 3–5000ohms (3–5kOhms) resistance when energised (i.e. supplied with power), creates a strong magnetic field at its centre. This field attracts up into the coil a soft iron rod or plunger, and will hold it in that position as long as power is supplied to the coil. When power is removed (de-energised) from the coil, a spring at the top of the plunger recess returns to its resting position.

Single valve: Red for hot supply. White for cold supply.

Double valve: Cold supply only. One side for pre-wash. Other for conditioner.

Triple valve: Generally cold supply, found on some automatic washers and dishwashers.

How does it work?

Shown here in detail are the two states of the water valve.

Fig. 5. The de-energised valve (at rest — no power supplied).
    With no power supplied to the solenoid coil (a), the soft iron core (b) is pressed firmly onto the centre hole of the flexible diaphragm by spring (c). As chamber (d) is only at atmospheric pressure and the water is at least 4lbs p.s.i. (somewhat higher), pressure is exerted on the top of the diaphragm*, effectively closing it tight. The greater the water pressure the greater the closing effect of the valve therefore no water will flow.

*The pressure on top of the diaphragm is via a small bleed hole marked (e). It is essential that this very small hole is not obstructed. Though very small, it is a major factor in the correct operation of these types of pressure operated valves.

Fig. 6. The energised valve (power supplied to it). When power is supplied to the solenoid coil, the resulting magnetic attraction of the coil overcomes the power of the spring (c) and pulls the plunger up into the coil centre. This allows an imbalance of pressure to occur by exposing the centre hole of the diaphragm. The imbalance lifts the flexible diaphragm and allows water to flow into chamber (d), thus water flow is achieved.
    It is easier for the water to lift the diaphragm than to balance the pressure by flowing through the very small bleed hole. Any enlargement or blockage of this vital bleed hole will render the valve inoperative.

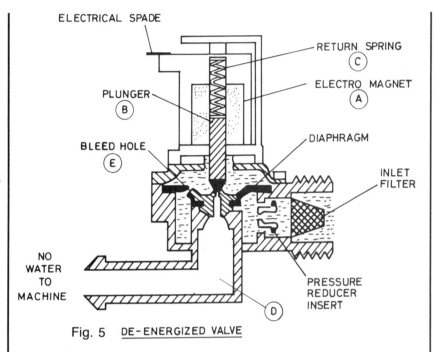

Fig. 5   DE-ENERGIZED VALVE

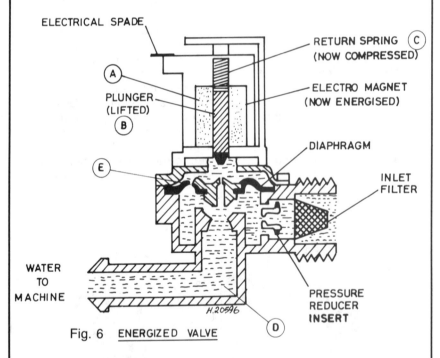

Fig. 6   ENERGIZED VALVE

Main benefits of such valves

1. The higher the pressure supplied to it the tighter the valve will close.
2. Cost is relatively low.
3. Very reliable.
4. Simple to change if faulty.

Typical faults to watch for

1. As with ordinary house taps, the valve seat may wear and allow a small trickle of water to pass even when de-energised. This will cause the machine to fill when not in use if the taps are left turned on over a long

period of time and the machine will overfill, resulting in a possible flood.

2. The valve, when de-energised, will fail to allow the plunger to return to its normal resting/closed position. This problem will cause severe overfill and flooding.

Note: Turning off the machine will not stop the overfilling in such cases. Complete isolation of both power and water supply is required and, as with step 1, complete renewal will be necessary.

3. The valve fails to allow water to flow due to open circuit in coil winding. See: *Electrical fault finding* in the *Using a meter* chapter.

4. The valve fails to allow water to flow due to a blocked filter on its inlet. Carefully remove and clean. Do not allow any particle, no matter how small to escape past the filter as it could block the bleed hole.

Water valves come in many sizes and an assortment of shapes, from single valves, double valves and triple valves or a combination of all three. On the double and triple valves, each solenoid operates one outlet from a common inlet. Unfortunately, a fault on one coil or one outlet will generally mean a complete renewal of the whole valve assembly, as individual spare parts are not available.

Verify the suspected fault

In this theoretical instance, the machine was loaded and a programme selected but it failed to fill. Moving the timer/control to a pump out position confirmed that power was being supplied and that the door interlock was working. See: *Door Switches (interlocks)* chapter. Box 1. Reselect wash programme to confirm that the machine was originally set and turned on correctly. With the machine correctly set. Box 2. confirms that, although the

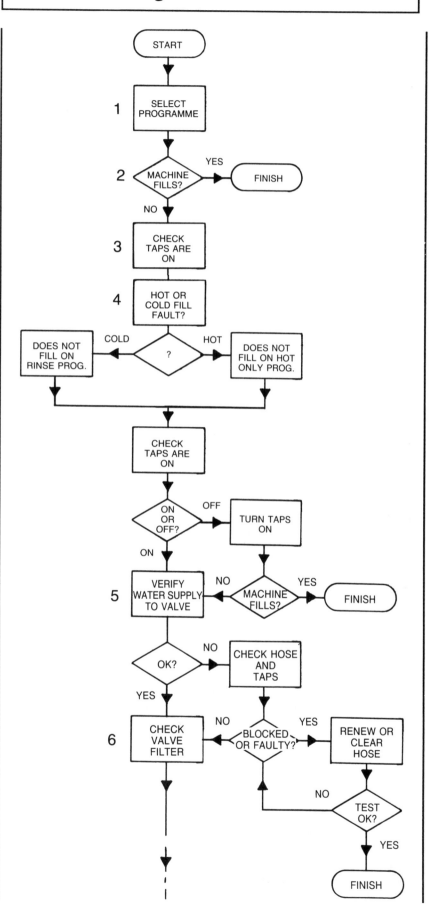

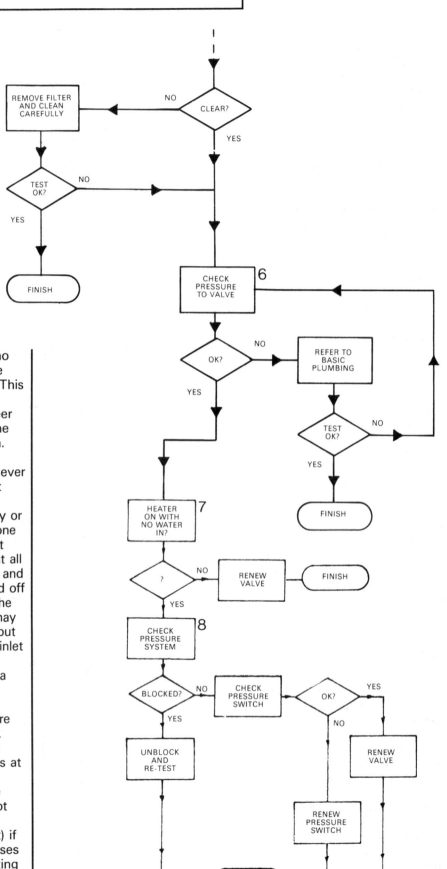

machine has electrical feed, no water is entering to begin the filling/washing action. Box 3. This may seem too obvious to mention, but many an engineer has been called out to find the taps were in the 'off' position. This normally brings the comment that the taps are 'never turned off', and in this case it must have been some other devious member of the family or innocent plumber that has done the dirty deed! This comment brings in the cardinal rule that all automatic washing machines and dishwashers should be turned off at their isolation taps when the machine is not in use. This may seem a quite pointless task, but the objective is simple. If an inlet pipe should split, or an inlet valve fails to close correctly, a quite disastrous flood could occur. This would not be the case however, if the taps were turned off between each use. Box 4. This section is to help identify which water supply is at fault, hot or cold. Normally whites-only washes fill at the start of a programme with hot water only, so selecting this programme will verify (or not) if the hot supply is at fault. Rinses use only cold water so selecting a rinse fill sequence will verify (or not) if the cold supply is at fault. See the chapter on *Functional testing* to assist in this task. Box 5. By unscrewing the hose from the valve, confirmation of water supply can be easily checked by turning the tap to which it is connected, on and off, ensuring that the free end of the hose is held in a suitable container. Failure of water flow could be due to a faulty tap or tap shaft or an internal fault of the supply hose. Some makers of machines supply rubber inlet hose seals which have a metal or gauze filter moulded into them. It is recommended in the manufacturer's instruction booklet, that the two washers supplied with the filters are fitted at the isolation tap end of the supply hose as a first line filter for the valves. Check if such filter washers were used during the original installation by unscrewing the supply hose from the isolation tap. Clean or renew

as required. Box 6. The checking of the water valve inlet filter can be carried out while the hose is removed from for Step 4. Take care not to allow any particles to escape past the fine mesh filter and into the valve. Carefully clean the filter of all scale and debris, etc., and replace. **Note:** The filter can be removed by gently gripping the centre with pliers and pulling it free of the main valve body. Box 7. Ensure that the water supply to the valve is adequate to operate the valve. See: *Basics – plumbing* chapter. Box 8 & 9. If the heater is found to be switched on when there is no water in the machine,

a pressure system fault is indicated and should be checked. Details of this process will be found in the *Water level control* chapter (pressure system) section. If the heater is in the off position when there is no water in the machine, the valve would appear to be suspect. The valve is easily changed by removing the fixing screws and detaching the internal hose/s from the valve. Making a note of the wiring and hose connections that are on the valve, remove them and replace with a new valve assembly by simply reconnecting the hoses and wires in a reverse sequence.

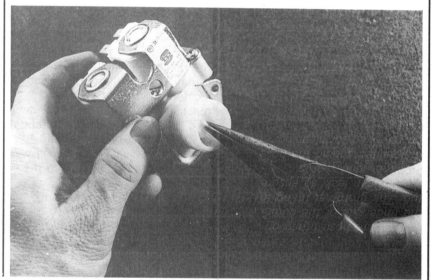

If the valve filter requires cleaning, carefully remove it as shown, ensuring that no debris slips past.

Once removed, the filter can be thoroughly cleaned and inspected for damage. **Note**: *This can be done with the valve in situ. It was removed in this instance for photographic purposes only.*

Chapter 18

Water level control

Modern automatic washing machines will have several fill levels each of which corresponds to the type of wash cycle selected, e.g. high level fill for delicate programmes and lower level for the more robust wash programmes. There may also be the facility for an intermediate level option if a half-load selection is available to the programme. The way in which the amount of water used for a selected programme is governed by a pressure system.

What is a pressure system?

The pressure system governs the level of water in the machine.

Where is it located?

The pressure switch has no standard fixture location, but is usually to be found at the top of the machine. It can be identified as the large circular switch that has several wires and a plastic tube attached to it leading to a pressure vessel. Several variations of pressure vessel are available. It may be an integral part of the plastic filter housing located behind the front face of

the machine's shell, alternatively it may be an independent unit located to the rear of the machine near the tub. There are also pressure hoses that function in the same way as the rigid pressure vessel. These hoses will either be grommet fitted to the lower part of the outer tub, or directly moulded to the sump hose. Machines that have moulded plastic outer tubs normally have provision for a rigid pressure vessel to be mounted on the lower section. Although the position and style of the switch and pressure vessels vary, the basic way in which they operate does not.

A typical pressure switch.

How does it work?

The pressure switch does not actually come into contact with water, but uses air pressure trapped within the pressure vessel or pressure hose. When water enters the tub and the level rises, it traps a given amount of air in the pressure vessel. As the water in the tub rises, this increases the pressure of the trapped air within the pressure vessel. This pressure is then transferred to a pressure

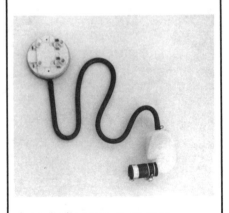

A typical pressure system.

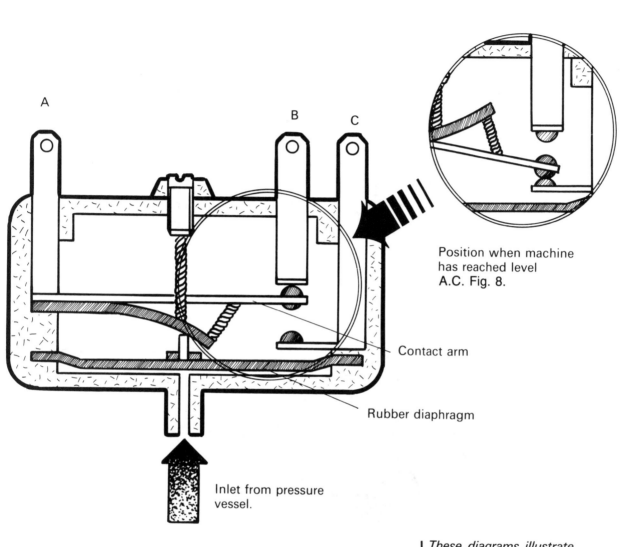

Position when machine has reached level A.C. Fig. 8.

Contact arm

Rubber diaphragm

Inlet from pressure vessel.

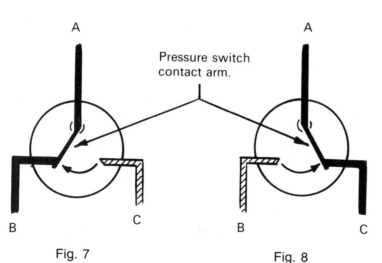

Pressure switch contact arm.

Fig. 7

Fig. 8

These diagrams illustrate the theoretical operation of a single level pressure switch. A. being the live supply. Point B. is the empty position of the pressure switch, and in this position power supplied to A via the programme timer would be allowed to flow to the fill valve via B. When the preset level of water is reached, the diaphragm of the pressure switch pushes the contact arm across to contact C. Power to the fill valve is therefore stopped and transferred to connection C. Fig. 8. which in turn could supply the main motor and heater.

sensitive switch via a small bore flexible tube.

The pressure switch is a large circular device that houses a thin rubber diaphragm, which is expanded by the corresponding pressure exerted on it. The diaphragm rests alongside a bank of up to three switches, each of which is set to operate at a different level of pressure. The switch is totally isolated from the water ensuring maximum safety.

Possible faults in the pressure region

To create the highest pressure in the chamber of the pressure vessel, the vessel must be positioned as low as possible in the machine. Unfortunately, any sediment that forms in the machine collects at this point and can therefore easily block the entrance. Similarly, because of its very small internal diameter, the pressure tube can also block. The pressure that this device creates is very small, and can easily be blocked by a very small obstruction, such as a lump

of power or sediment deposits.

The seals and hoses of the system are also of great importance. These should be checked for air leaks and blockages. Any puncture or blockage would create a loss of pressure, resulting in the incorrect operation of the switches, i.e., if the air pressure in the pressure vessel were to leak out, the vessel would fill with water. Indicating that the machine was in fact empty, the water valves would be re-energised, thus trying to fill an already full machine. The results would be obvious.

The above example assumed that the air was prevented from actuating the pressure switch. If a blockage occurred whilst the switch was pressurised, the machine would work as normal until the machine emptied. The next time a programme was started the pressure switch would already be pressurised. Therefore the

Typical pressure hose.

Photograph showing the position of the pressure switch in a typical automatic. The positions may vary with makes, but all will be found as high in the machine as possible.

Showing the pressure vessel used on machines such as Hoover, Creda and early Servis machines.

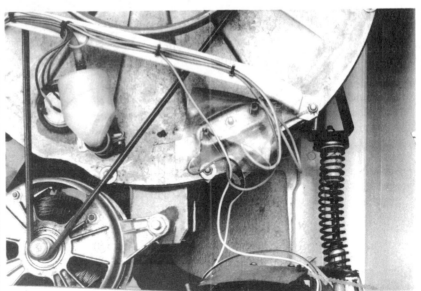

machine would not take any water, but proceed to turn the heater on. Although most heaters are now fitted with a T.O.C. (Thermal Overload Cut-out – see *Jargon*), this may not act until some damage has been done to the clothes inside the drum.

Points to note

(a) The pressure system should be checked at yearly or half-yearly intervals, depending on the water hardness in your area.
(b) Any hoses or tubes that have been disturbed must be resealed, and any clips tightened.
(c) Blowing down the accessible end of the pressure tube may seem an easy solution to remove a blockage, but this may only be a temporary cure. Also, water may enter the pressure vessel before you can push the end of the tube back onto the pressure switch. This will render the pressure system inaccurate, if not useless.

A pressure switch should only be suspected when the system has been thoroughly cleaned, checked, sealed and re-tested.

Checking a pressure switch

Blowing into the switch via the pressure tube, the audible 'clicks' of the switches should be heard. This should also happen when the pressure is released. If your

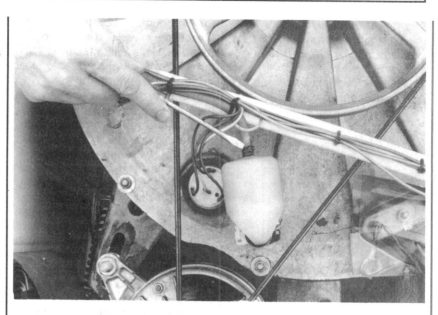

Any loose connections on the pressure system will allow the pressure to drop. This will cause overfilling. Ensure a good seal.

machine uses a single level of water, one click will be heard. Two levels of water will produce two clicks. If your machine has an economy button, a third faint click will also be heard. **Note:** Do not blow too hard as this may damage the switch. Remember, the pressure they operate on is very low.

An internal view of a pressure switch, showing the diaphragm and switches. This pressure switch was faulty due to a small hole appearing in the internal diaphragm. Operation would appear correct, although the pressure would decrease during the wash, and the machine would overfill. If the first functional test was rushed, this type of fault could be overlooked. The switch in the picture was stripped down to confirm the fault only. These switches require replacement when faulty, as they cannot be repaired.

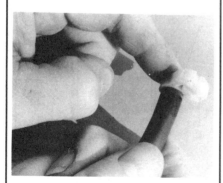

Check the pressure tube for chafing and small porous cracks. Renew if suspect.

The figure below illustrates the way a 3 level switch is used in conjunction with an economy switch, to give an alternative level as an economy feature.

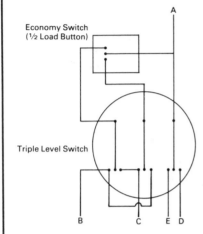

Economy Switch
(½ Load Button)

Triple Level Switch

A

B   C   E   D

Many machines have an overfill level detection system which will activate the outlet pump should any excess water enter the machine for any reason. Several systems use the third or fourth switch of the existing pressure switch bank, operated only by the increased pressure caused by the overfill.

Unfortunately, systems that use the same pressure vessel for both normal and abnormal water level detection may fail to detect overfilling if it is caused by a blocked pressure vessel or hose fault that allows the pressure to escape.

Systems using a separate pressure vessel and a separate pressure switch for detecting overfilling are much less prone to failure of this nature. Nevertheless, they still require cleaning and checking frequently.

Main faults within the pressure switch

(a) When the diaphragm becomes 'holed' or porous, the switch can be operated and clicks heard, but will click back again without being de-pressurised.

(b) The contact points inside the switch may 'weld' themselves together. This will alter the number of clicks heard, as one or more may be inoperative. Movement of the switch can free the points, although this will not be a lasting repair, as the switch will fail again.

Any of the above faults require the fitting of a new switch. The make, model and serial number of the machine should be stated when ordering, as pressure switches are internally pre-set for specific machines, although the external appearance is similar. Fitting is a simple direct exchange between the old and new.

The diagram illustrates the operation of a double level pressure switch. Fig. 1 shows the machine filling with water. If B and E are taken as hot and cold valves respectively, it can be seen that the machine is filling with both of the valves. In Fig. 2 the lowest level of water is reached. The pressure breaks the connection with the hot valve (B), and remakes it with the heater switch (C). The cold valve (E) continues filling. Fig. 3 shows

the highest level, with the cold fill stopping, switching in the motor (D). Fig. 4 illustrates the way a 3 level switch is used in conjunction with an economy switch, to give an alternative level as an economy feature.

The diagram below illustrates the theoretical operation of a double level pressure switch. Fig. 1 shows the machine filling with water. If B and E are taken as hot and cold valves respectively, it can be seen that the machine is filling with both hot and cold water. In Fig. 2 the lowest level of water is reached. The pressure breaks the connection with the hot valve (B), and remakes it with the heater switch (C). The cold valve (E) continues filling. Fig. 3 shows the highest level, with the cold fill stopping switching in the motor (D).

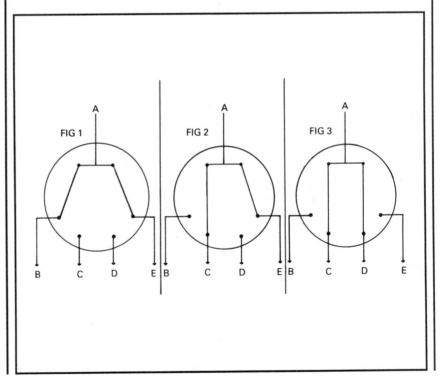

FIG 1   A

B   C   D   E

FIG 2   A

B   C   D   E

FIG 3   A

B   C   D   E

Clearing a pressure system blockage

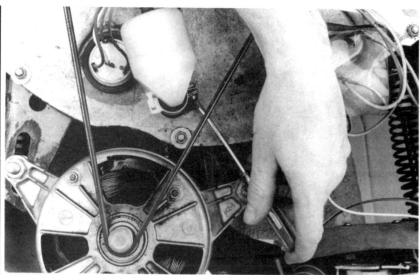

1. Note and remove all connections to the pressure switch. Remove complete system from machine.

2. Check connecting hose for blockages at both ends and blow down tube to check for air leaks and to clear if of any obstructions.

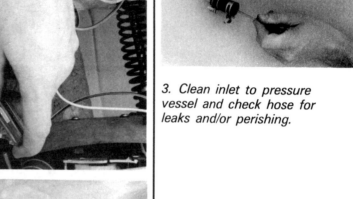

3. Clean inlet to pressure vessel and check hose for leaks and/or perishing.

4. Carefully check outlet of pressure vessel for any build up of sludge.

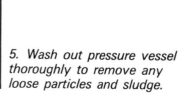

5. Wash out pressure vessel thoroughly to remove any loose particles and sludge.

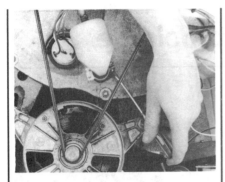

6. Check the pressure tube and any rubber hose connections for wear (i.e., rubbing on pulley, belt or clips.)

8. The typical position of a pressure switch on an Indesit machine.

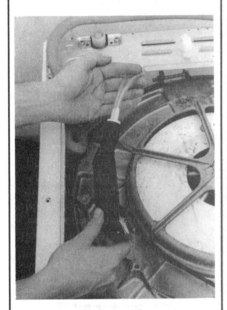

7. Pressure hose fitting on the underside of the outer tub. The grommet fitting to the tub can leak, so ensure that the good seal is maintained should the hose be removed for cleaning.

9. A front fitting pressure vessel of the type used for Hotpoint machines.

10. A pressure vessel inside a top loading machine. This vessel is held in position by a plastic nut, which is only accessible from inside the tub. This requires the removal of the outer shell and top surface. Note the sediment at the bottom of the pressure vessel.

A similar procedure should be followed for all types of pressure vessel and care should be taken to re-seal all hose connections that are removed. Remember to wash clear all loose particles, etc., as even the smallest of blockages in this system will cause trouble.

11. Integral pressure vessel and filter. These units are difficult to clean thoroughly so care is required. Also ensure a good seal on the pressure tube when refitting.

12. This picture shows a pressure vessel which is much longer than usual. Most vessels are much smaller. This type can be found in Candy and Newpol machines (pressure vessel arrowed).

Pressure switch types

1. Typical single level switch that is fitted to many basic machines.

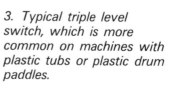

2. Typical double level switch is more common.

3. Typical triple level switch, which is more common on machines with plastic tubs or plastic drum paddles.

4. Variable pressure switch as fitted to early Hotpoint top loader machines. The centre button changes the pressure required to operate the diaphragm. This is linked (mechanically) to the wash load select buttons on the control panel.

5. Some pressure switches may have their tube connections on the rear plate. This is only a variation on the fixing type, and does not impair the operation of the switch.

Chapter 19

Pumps

For details of the motors used to power the pump, see *Motors* chapter.

The pump is a vital part of the correct functioning of the machine and prone to various faults. Leaks from the pump may not be apparent, but the resulting pool of water usually is. So here are a few points to look out for.

Firstly check all clips on the hoses to and from the pump and tighten if they are loose.

If the leak remains, the pump's shaft seal should be checked. This is the seal that forms a water tight barrier on the rotating shaft of the motor directly between the impeller, and the front motor bearing. The seal can be broken by a collection of fluff/lint forming between the seal and the impeller itself, thus distorting the rubber seal. To check if this is happening, remove the pump chamber, by removing its securing clips or screws, and whilst securing the rotor of the pump motor, turn the impeller clockwise to undo it from the shaft, i.e., impeller and rotor are usually left-hand threaded. Having done this, remove any objects adhering to the shaft and refit, ensuring the pump chamber

seal is in position. If the seal still leaks this will be due to it being worn or softened. On most machines, this means the complete renewal of the pump. (Not so costly as you may think, as many genuine and proprietary pumps of good quality are now available at very low cost.)

This may seem drastic for such a small seal, but the fact is that water containing detergent would have been entering the front pump bearing long before the leak was bad enough to see. This means it will probably be damaged itself and next in line to cause trouble.

The only type of pump where complete renewal can be avoided is the 'late' Hoover type, with a large flat disc type seal, that is the pump chamber seal, and the shaft seal in one. If the seal has leaked, the front bearing should be replaced at the same time as the seal. If the rotor shaft was found to be worn, (even slightly, i.e., roughness/scoured), it would probably be easier and quicker to fit a complete compatible pump, to avoid any further trouble. In fact this could be the least expensive remedy.

Other leaks can be attributable to the pump, (i.e.,

due to impeller damage. That is to say blades of impeller broken off or badly worn away by a solid object lodged in the pump at sometime, e.g. small coin or tight bearings causing slow running of motor).

Both of the above will result in poor water discharge, i.e., slow draining. This in turn may cause the machine to spin whilst some water still remains, thus causing other hoses, etc., on the machine to leak or the machine to fill to too high a level, as some machines have a timed rinse fill action. On other machines, slow drainage may mean that the machine fails to spin at all. This is due to the pressure switch detecting the presence of water in the machine, (that the slow pump failed to discharge in its allotted time), therefore not allowing a spin to take place and either missing out the spin completely or stopping the wash cycle at the spin positions.

Checking the impeller and bearings can be done at the same time as checking the seal.

Most automatics are fitted with electric pumps – exceptions are the basic version of the Indesit automatics (L5, L7, L8 range). These have what is called

Breakdown of Indesit manual pump.

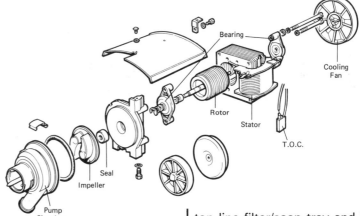

a 'mechanical' pump.

That is to say that the pump is not a separate unit, but is attached to the rear of the main motor, and therefore runs continually in conjunction with the main motor.

This however does not mean that the machine empties when the motor runs at wash speed. Pump action only occurs on the spin speed, when the motor runs at full speed in only one direction. This means that this type of machine actually spins whilst still full of water. Good seals on door boots and all internal hoses and grommets are therefore essential to avoid leaks.

The same problems of leaks on the shaft-mounted seal are encountered on this type of pump and are even more pronounced as the pump shaft is turning for most of the wash cycle.

With leaks on this type of pump, it is essential that it should be stopped, and the fault rectified to avoid damage to the main motor.

The repair to this type of pump is quite simple. The impeller, (much larger and more solid in this case) is secured by a left-hand threaded bolt. A kit for repairing this type of pump is available with all relevant parts.

A pump that operates in a similar fashion to that of the above, is that found in the Hotpoint top-loader automatics. This is also driven by the main motor, but with this machine on wash action, the pump is used to circulate water through the

top line filter/soap tray and has an 'empty only' cycle before allowing the machine to spin.

Faults found with this pump include shaft seal leaking, (this damages the bearing and allows sideways movement of the shaft and also, due to its position above the main motor, water is spread widely in the machine casing by the motor's cooling fan). Also wearing of an internal rubber flap valve occurs. This causes the machine to empty slightly on wash cycles, thus lengthening the programme time.

This pump is a complete replacement item, and two versions are available. Large pulley drive, for early machines, and small pulley drive ($\frac{3}{4}$ inch diameter, 2 cm approximately) for late machines.

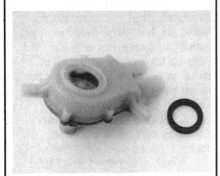

Manual pump of this type found on Hotpoint top loader automatic.

Indesit type electric pump will fit early machines and dishwashers.

Typical electric pump with sump hose and outlet hose of the type found on many of the leading makes. The main differences with electric pumps are the pump chamber mouldings. All pumps empty at about 6 to 8 gallons per minute.

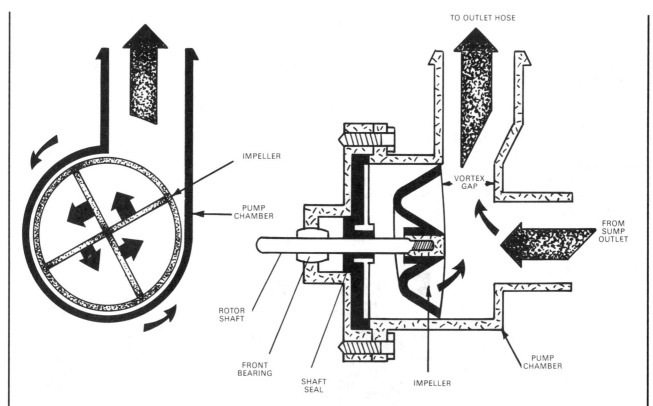

Vortex style pump.
Dynamic force exerted on the water in the direction of the outlet.

Above is a simple illustration of the outlet pump chamber and impeller. Water from the sump enters from the front. The rotation of the impeller lifts the water in the direction of the narrower outlet hose.

There are two types of impeller; one is simply a paddle type and more prone to blockages: the second is like the one illustrated and called a vortex pump. This type of impeller is more of a flat etched disc that allows a gap between itself and the pump chamber. This gap lets particles pass through easier than the bladed impeller version. The vortex impeller applies lift to the water as shown in the smaller version, the action is similar to the rotating vortex created when a bath empties.

Typical pump replacement

Note: Ensure that the machine is isolated before attempting any repair on your washing machine.

In the following sequence of pictures we show the location of the pump assembly on a Hoover 1100 automatic, although it is fair to say that the pump and its location is almost standard throughout the Hoover range.

The machine was leaking badly when inspected, but was in fact still working. When questioned, the user admitted

1. Ensure that machine is isolated and remove rear panel. Note location of pump – Back, right-hand corner.

that the machine had been leaking for some considerable time, but now more water seemed to be leaking out than ever before. As you may see, this is obvious in pictures 3 & 4, by the degree of corrosion to both pump and the shell of the machine. (This level of corrosion would have been avoided by earlier detection/report of the earlier, much smaller leak.)

Shown in pictures 5 & 6 are variations of pumps that may be encountered on this type of machine. Pictures 7 to 12 show the further stripdown of the pump. In this case, it was thought best to renew the pump completely owing to the amount of water and detergent damage to both the bearings and metal laminations of the stator. (Again this would have been avoided, if the earlier leak had been dealt with sooner.)

The complete pump of the type shown in picture 6 was fitted, and the shell and mounts were coated with anti-rust compound prior to the fitting of the pump. Care must be taken that the anti-corrosion liquid does not come into contact with any rubber hoses or seals.

After replacing all hoses and connections (a simple reversal of the removal procedure) the machine was re-positioned into its correct working position and was re-connected to the water and power supply. A functional

test was carried out to ensure that the new pump functioned correctly, to ensure that the re-positioned clips were water-tight and that no other leaks or faults were present.

At this point, the user was advised of the unnecessary danger (and danger in this case) caused by using the machine when it obviously had a fault that was ignored.

Note: In most modern machines, the pump has to be changed as a complete unit for even the smallest of problems. This is no

excuse for turning a blind eye to such faults. Such behaviour is false economy.

The anti-corrosion coat mentioned can be one of many types available from DIY car centres and hardware shops. Please use as per manufacturer's instructions, taking care not to allow any contact with rubber hoses or plastics. When using anti-corrosion gel or rubber sealant indoors, care should be taken to protect the floor from spillage, and ensure that adequate ventilation is available.

3. Note and remove the hose clips and connections. Corrosion may be found on the mounting. At this point treat with anti-rust compound prior to refitting.

5. Shown are two types of Hoover pump that may be found. (Different styles of impeller and stator).

4. Support pump whilst removing securing bolts and withdraw pump from machine.

2. Machine face protected and carefully laid over. Position of pump now clearly visible.

6. This type of 'pattern' pump will fit Hoover, Creda, Servis and Hotpoint. Many other styles are available for other machines.

7. Lever small clips loose using small bladed screwdriver. Hold clip lightly to prevent it springing off. Screws may be found in place of clips.

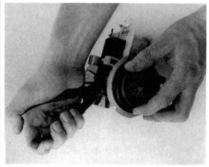

9. Whilst holding rear shaft securely, turn impeller clockwise and remove. (LH thread).

11. Seal removed and front bearing checked for wear and damage. Also check rear bearing.

8. Note pump chamber position and remove to expose impeller.

10. Rear seal exposed. In this case it is badly worn by a build up of lint upon shaft.

12. Rear view of seal showing extensive wear.

13. When fitting a new pump as in this instance, check the bolt hole sizes of the mounting plate. On some occasions they may need enlarging.

15. Reconnect the terminals. If the pump has an earth tag, ensure that it is a good fit, as with all connections.

17. When the hoses and clips have been re-fitted, the machine is ready for testing on the rinse cycle. Ensure all panels are refitted before commencing functional testing.

14. Secure pump firmly into position.

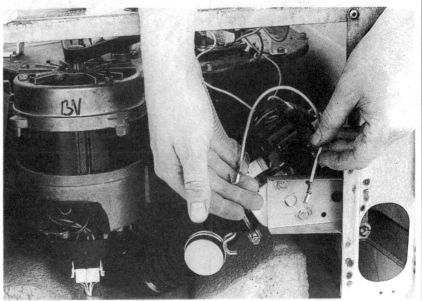

16. If a pump has a plastic mounting plate, it is essential that the metal stator laminations are linked to the machine earth path. Make a short lead to connect the earth tag on the pump to the fixing bolt and secure firmly.

Chapter 20

Door switches (interlocks)

What is an interlock?

The name interlock is given to an electrical switch behind or near the main door latching device of washing machines and is designed to give a time delay of up to two minutes, before the door can be opened. The delay time differs between the makes and models of different machines.

Zanussi 3DB style interlock.

Later Bendix 7TAG square interlock.

What are the different types?

A machine with a push/pull timer knob action, may also have a manual interlock thus giving double protection. The manual interlock system is quite straightforward, bolting or unbolting the door with the push/pull action of the timer knob, via a latching mechanism. The mechanical interlock acts in much the same way as the electrical version in preventing entry via the door if the machine is turned on except that there is no time delay. Such mechanical interlocks are always in addition to electrical interlocks which incorporate a delay to entry.
    A more recent version of interlock also incorporates a

Philips style 3DB interlock.

pressure switch type of system, that will not allow the door to open if there is any water remaining in the machine. This again is a mechanical operation and will work even when the machine is unplugged. The door can only be opened when the water has been drained out. This must be remembered in the case of a pump failure or blockage. The system is easily recognisable by the pressure tube leading to the door interlock. Such systems may use a separate pressure vessel or a 'T' junction arrangement from the water level pressure switch tube. Whichever system is used, faults similar to those described in the water level control chapter will be encountered, e.g., blockages, air leaks, etc.

How does a basic interlock work?

Because manufacturers prefer to have their own version of interlock, it is impossible to illustrate all of the different types. Because of this, the Klixon (3DB) type of switch is used to illustrate the internal workings and theory.

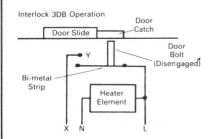

Fig. 1. Diagram A.

Diagram A shows the state of the interlock before power at L. It can be seen that the door bolt is disengaged and the bi-metal strip is in its 'rest' position. Because of this, there is no connection at point Y, therefore no power is transmitted to X.

Diagram B shows the state of the interlock when power is applied to point L. The heater is activated, therefore heating the bi-metal strip. This then bends, engaging the door bolt and making the connection at Y, allowing power to flow to X. When the power is disconnected, the heater is allowed to cool and the bi-metal strip then bends back to it rest position. This action can take up to two minutes, thus creating the delay. The delay time (cooling of heater and bi-metal) will vary according to the ambient temperature, style of interlock and position of the appliance. Some makes and variations of interlocks use a small oil-filled piston

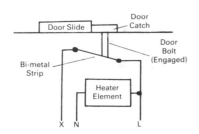

Fig. 2. Diagram B.

Hoover style 1DB.

One variation of a three tag 3DB interlock (Klixon). Shown is the early Hoover 800/1100 variant.

7 Tag 'rectangular' interlock usually found on a Bendix machine, this can be interhcanged with a 7 tag 'square' interlock.

Early style Indesit 3 tag 'rectangular' interlock.

The 'Rold' interlock is becoming increasingly popular with today's manufacturers. Shown is the Fagor variant. Also found in Indesit machines.

arrangement in place of the bi-metal strip. When heated, the oil expands and the resulting piston movement is used to actuate the interlock. As with the bi-metal system described, cooling allows the piston to retract and de-latch the interlock.

Note: The heater referred to in this part of the manual is not the large heater in the drum, but is of minute proportions and is only used to heat the bi-metal strip.

Modern machines tend to link the interlock to all of the other functions of the machines, so if the interlock should fail, power to the rest of the machine would be severed and the machine would then be totally inoperable. With older machines, interlock failure would only result in no motor action throughout a normal programme.

A two tag interlock (1DB) is shown. The 1DB being called a straight through interlock as, although locking occurs, switching does not. (Many Candy machines use a smaller version of this type of interlock mounted on the switch panel directly behind the door opening button. When the interlock is actuated

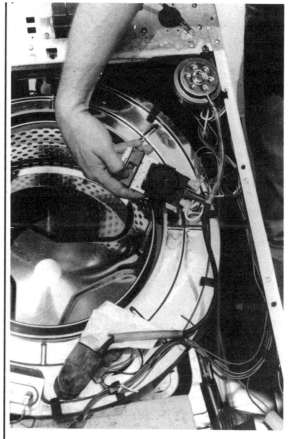

New style interlock with pressure lock included. This works in conjunction with the pressure switch, and does not allow the door to open if any water remains in the machine.

Internal view of an interlock that uses a sealed piston arrangement in place of a bi-metal strip. The piston can be seen at the base of the unit passing through the large return spring on the left and resting on the circular heater pod on the right.

operation of the door opening button is prevented.)

Note: The delay time is needed for the continued spinning of the drum after the motor has turned off, and is now a legal requirement. For this reason they **must not** be by-passed, as the results to small children or impatient adults **will** be disastrous.

7 Tag 'square' interlock, which can be found in Bendix machines. 3 or 5 tag interlocks can also be found.

Interlocks (computer controlled)

Computer controlled machines (as opposed to mechanically controlled) may have similar electro-mechanical interlocks to

those described in the previous paragraphs. Alternatively, depending on make and model, they could be completely different both in the way the door is opened and the way that access is restricted via the door until the programme has finished and the machine is completely empty of water. A breakdown of basic operation is as follows though it does not typify any specific make as manufacturers will incorporate subtle differences to create individuality of product.

Door opening is by means of a push button action that actuates a simple electrical switch which then makes contact and supplies power to a solenoid-operated catch mounted within the machine in place of the door interlock. With power supplied to the solenoid in this way the door latch is released and the door opens. To avoid continuous supply to the solenoid, a microswitch is incorporated within the unit to open circuit the solenoid coil as soon as the door latch pecker is released. The opening operation of the door depends on:

1. Power being supplied to the machine and the machine being turned on.
2. No programme is currenty operating.
3. No motor action or drum rotation is taking place.
4. Any water in the machine is below the lowest detectable level of the pressure switch, i.e.,

all switches in rest position. See: *Water level control* chapter.
5. Door open button is released.

The requirements of steps 2–5 are monitored continuously by the microprocessor within the electronically controlled timer. With condition 1, a power supply is necessary for the door solenoid to operate. However, in power failure or fault situations, many machines have means of de-latching the door mechanism manually; reference should be made to the appliance handbook for further information. Before carrying out mechanical actuation of the latch, ensure the machine is unplugged (isolated) and that the water level is below the door level, see: *Emergency procedures* and photo in this chapter.

Several machines use an LED (light emitting diode) or display to indicate when door opening can be activated.

The use of a microprocessor within such machines allows for greater interaction and sensing to be carried out. Due to the larger memory size of the chips used, more variable programming is possible. The way in which the programme is written enables it to react to variations within the circuit of the machine which in turn gives rise to a greater number of criteria being monitored to ensure compliance with safety, etc. The microprocessor board also includes a clock chip which can help in controlling programme times and functions

accurately. The timing function can also be used to time a delay to the door open switch if required by the manufacturer of the machine.

Shown is only a small selection of interlocks to highlight the many variations that can be encountered. Interlocks cannot only change between machine manufacturers, but the models themselves may have different variants, i.e., machines with identical external appearance may have different variants of the interlock fitted.

The outer design and fitting of the interlock may change, but the function and operations differs very little between variants.

One type of interlock may be common to more than one manufacturer. It is therefore essential to obtain the correct model and serial numbers of both the machine and interlock when locating a spare part.

A typical electro-mechanical interlock as fitted to computer controlled machines. The cord is for manual operation in case of electrical supply failure or fault.

Shown is a machine with twin pressure switches and a pressure operated door interlock. The 'T' junction can be seen between the two circular pressure switches. The tube to the top right-hand side leads down to the door interlock (not shown).

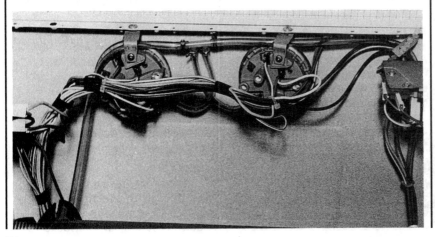

Chapter 21

The heater

Where is the wash water heater located?

The wash water heater is usually located in the lower part of the tub assembly, and can be either fitted through the back half of the tub or through an aperture in the tub base itself. One exception to this is the Hotpoint front loader range where the heater is located on the front of the outer tub, directly below the door seal. Access is gained by removing the front panel of the machine. Details of this are to be found in the *Door seal* chapter.

Removal and refitting of the heater

After making a note of the connections and removing them, the heater can be withdrawn from its position by slackening, but not removing the centre nut, and tapping it to release the tension then gently easing the rubber grommet free from its position with a flat-bladed screwdriver. Refitting is a reversal of these instructions, although a little sealant should be applied to both surfaces of the grommet fitting. Care should be taken that the centre nut is not overtightened, as this would cause a distortion of the metal plate. On most automatic washing machines, the inner of the outer tub has a raised flange or cover plate that engages the curved section at the end of the heater. It is important that this is located correctly when refitting the heater. Check that it is located and held correctly by pressing firmly but carefully downwards on the terminals of the heater whilst slowly rotating the inner drum. If the heater is not located correctly it will pivot on the grommet mounting and allow the element to come into contact with the drum, resulting in a grating noise and vibration. If such a noise is experienced during this simple test, slacken the heater clamp centre nut, remove the heater completely and relocate it correctly, then try again.

Note: Do not exert excessive pressure on the terminals of the heater. Try to press down on the exposed outer sheath.

Machines that have plastic or nylon outer tubs are fitted with overheat protectors. These are essential and are linked in line with the live feed to the heater. They are fitted for safety reasons, for if a pressure switch or pressure system were to fail, it is possible for the heater to be engaged with no water in the tub.

This would be most unwelcome in a machine with a metal tub, although only minor damage would be caused to the clothes. If this type of fault were to happen in a plastic/nylon tub, the result would be extremely dangerous. **Note:** Under no circumstances should the overheat protection device be removed or bypassed.

The overheat protector that is used on early Philips machines was an integral part of the heater and is similar to a capillary thermostat switch. However, on later machines, a simple thermostat is used to open circuit the heater if overheat occurs. On the latest machines the thermostat is connected in the live supply between the door interlock to the pressure switch. If overheat occurs the thermostat goes open circuit and cuts power to all other components apart from the door interlock. Hotpoint use a separate thermal fuse heater protector for boil dry protection of their plastic outer tub machines and this item along with the late Philips thermostat are available separately.

If such items are found to be faulty, the result would be failure to heat the wash water or failure to move through the programme. If any type of protector is found to be open circuit, it is essential that the cause is identified and rectified prior to renewal. Thoroughly check the pressure system and switch. For more detailed information on thermal fuses and protection devices see the following *Temperature control* chapter.

Temperature control

There are several ways in which the temperature is controlled, details of which can be found in the following chapter.

Main faults with heaters

One of the most common faults with heaters, is that of open circuit, i.e., no current flows through the heater, therefore no heat is produced. This can simply be due to a broken or loose connection to one of the heater terminals. This then overheats, leaving an obvious discoloration of the connection or terminal, resulting in a break of the circuit at that point. Alternatively, the break in the circuit can occur within the element itself. Heaters can easily be tested for continuity as described in the – *Using a meter* chapter.

Another fault that can occur is that of low insulation. In this case, please refer to the chapter – *Low insulation*. Accompanying the low insulation fault is that of short circuiting of the heater caused by a complete breakdown of insulation of the element. This results in the appliance blowing fuses or earth tripping if an R.C.D. is in circuit.

Should any of the above faults occur, a complete replacement of the component(s) is required.

A few of the many variations of heaters

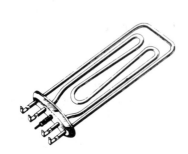

Zanussi Double 2 kw 700 w.

Indesit L Series.

Bendix 2 kw also Philco 2 grommet size available.

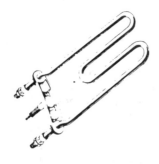

Zanussi 2.4 kw single.

Candy Type.

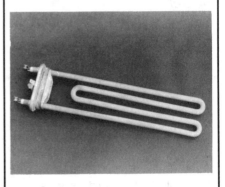

Normal style heater. (Do not fit to plastic tub machines).

Heater with overheat detector (arrowed). This is found on machines with plastic outer tubs.

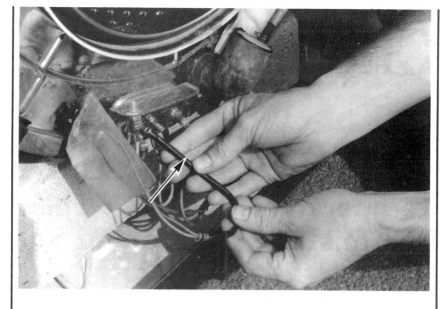

Overheated terminal due to loose connection on live supply.

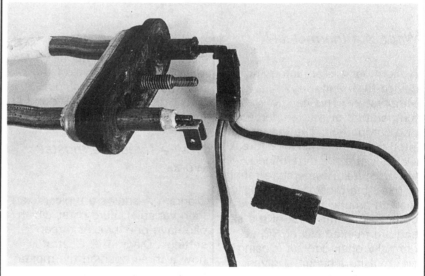

Scaling can lead to element failure. The degree of scaling varies depending on the hardness of the water and the detergent used.

Chapter 22

Temperature Control – Thermostats, Thermistors, T.O.C.s and Thermal Fuses

What is a thermostat?

A thermostat is an automatic device for monitoring temperature. This can be water temperature or the temperature of a component. The thermostat (stat) will either 'make' or 'break' a circuit at a pre-determined temperature. Temperature ratings of fixed thermostats are usually marked around the metal perimeter on the back of the stat and are marked NO or NC, i.e. normally open contact (closing and making a circuit at given temperature), or normally closed (opening at given temperature). Some thermostats can and do contain both variants. See diagrams.

Where are they located?

Positioning of each thermostat depends on the job it has to do. The wash temperature thermostat is usually located on the back half or underside of the outer tub depending on the make and model of the machine. Exceptions to this are the Hotpoint and Fagor front loading machines, where the thermostat, heater and pressure vessel are located on the front of the outer tub, directly below the door seal. Access to these components is gained by the removal of the front panel of the machine. Details of this are to be found in the *Door seal* chapter.

How a fixed thermostat works

Diagram A shows a typical fixed (non variable) thermostat which can have one, two or three settings. Diagram B illustrates how a three position thermostat works. The power enters the switch at X, but cannot proceed as there is no contact. As the temperature rises and each preset temperature is reached, the bi-metal disc set to that temperature bends, making one of the three possible contacts.

Removing and refitting a standard type thermostat

After making a note of the connections on the back, disconnect the wires from the rear of the thermostat. Insert a small screwdriver at point (Z), and prise the thermostat away from its grommet fitting. When refitting, it is advisable to smear

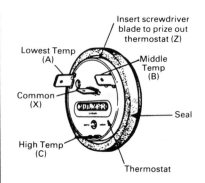

Diagram (A).

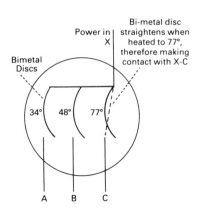

Diagram (B).

a little sealant on the grommet to aid correct fitting and avoid leaks. Refitting is a reversal of the removal process. **Note:** Before the removal or repair of any component from the machine, isolate the machine from the main electrical supply by removing the plug from the wall socket.

The diagrams show an alternative style of fixed thermostat, in this instance a 50°C. (NO) normally open contact and a 85°C (NC) normally closed contact. The latter is a safety thermostat which operates if overheating should occur within the machine.

The diagram illustrates the position of the thermostat at rest. Bi-metal discs are mounted directly behind the metal front cover of the stat and are preset to distort at given temperature (in this instance, 50°C and 85°C). They are linked to contact switches by pushrods. Any corresponding distortions of the discs, either make or break the corresponding contacts as shown.

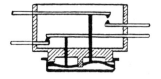

AT REST POSITION

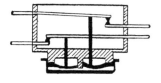

50° TEMP REACHED

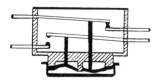

OVERHEAT SUPPLY TO HEATER DIRECT CUT OFF

When removed from the machine, the thermostat's operation can be tested by placing the metal cover in contact with a known heat source, e.g. radiator, hot water, etc., which matches or slightly exceeds the required temperature. Allow a little time for the heat to warm the stat and bi-metal discs. Testing for closing or opening of the thermostat can now be carried out as shown in the *Using a meter* chapter.

Check temperature with a household thermometer and allow a few degrees either way of the marked temperature on the outer rim of the stat, and remember to check if the stat is normally NO or NC. When cool, check that the stat returns to its normal position as indicated on the rim, i.e. NO or NC.

Removing and refitting

Make a note of the position, orientation and connections of the thermostat and then disconnect the wires. Insert a small flat-bladed screwdriver between the inner rubber lip and the metal front plate of the stat and prise the stat from the grommet. Care will be required if sealant has previously been used as this will have glued the stat into position. When refitting, it is advisable to smear a little sealant on the grommet to aid fitting and avoid leaks.

Refitting is a reversal of the removal process. See diagrams C, D, E.

To refit

Locate the metal lip in the grommet recess (D) and with the aid of a flat-bladed screwdriver ease the outer lip over the metal lip of the stat (C). Sealant will help locate and seal the thermostat into position, (E). Ensure that the thermostat is securely located into the

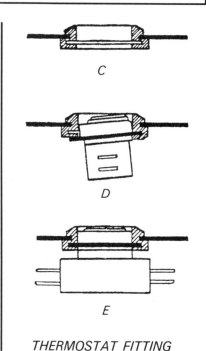

THERMOSTAT FITTING

grommet and that the outer lip is not trapped.

Thermostats may also be held in position by metal clips or clamps, and again, make sure of a good seal and check that the clips or clamps do not trap or touch any wires or connectors.

The variable thermostat

This is how a variable thermostat works. Diagram F shows a pod type thermostat. This is found on machines that have a variable wash temperature control. Diagram G is a schematic diagram of the internal workings. This consists of an oil- or gas-filled pod which is connected to the switch by a capillary tube. When the oil/gas in the pod is heated it expands within the sealed system and pushes a diaphragm. The diaphragm acts on the switchgear thus 'breaking' one circuit and 'making' the other. When the oil/gas cools it contracts, pulling the switch in the opposite direction. The switch is then in its original position and the process repeats if necessary.

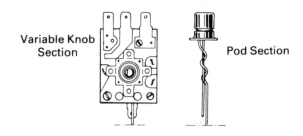

Diagram (F) – Typical pod type thermostat.

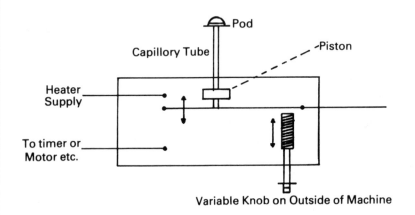

Diagram (G) – Internal workings of pod type thermostat.

the heater terminals or moving parts such as the main drivebelt. When fitted, the tube should be checked along its entire length for any possible contact with these items. Also, a coiled section of at least two large turns should be left at a convenient position to absorb the movement of the tub assembly. See diagrams F and G.

Testing a thermostat

The standard thermostat can be subjected to a known temperature (e.g. radiator, kettle, etc.) and be checked with a small test meter for continuity. This process is shown in the chapter *Using a meter*. The pod thermostat can be tested as above, ensuring that only the pod itself is immersed in water. **Note:** Whilst at room temperature, the state of the thermostat should be determined. On pod thermostats, the lowest and highest setting should be selected. During testing, ensure that switch actuates both on rise and fall of temperature, see chapter *Using a meter*.

Removing and refitting a pod type thermostat

The pod, which is located at the base of the capillary tube, must be eased from its rubber grommet gently, taking care not to unduly kink or pull on the capillary tube itself. **Note:** When fitting or refitting this form of thermostat, the capillary tube must not come into contact with any electrical contacts such as

Thermostat operation flowchart

Using the following flowchart, trace the sequence of events:

1 The machine is turned on.
2 The timer impulses, fills the machine with cold water and turns the heater on.
3-4 The thermostat 'waits' until the heater has heated the water to 40°C.
5-6 When the thermostat closes (i.e., the water has reached 40°C, the timer washes for two minutes. The timer starts the washing action for two minutes. (At this point the heater is still engaged).
7-8 The above operation is repeated, again with the heater engaged. When the two minute wash has ended, the water will be 45°C due to the extra four minute heating.
9-11 The timer then moves to the next position, which disengages the heater and would then be ready

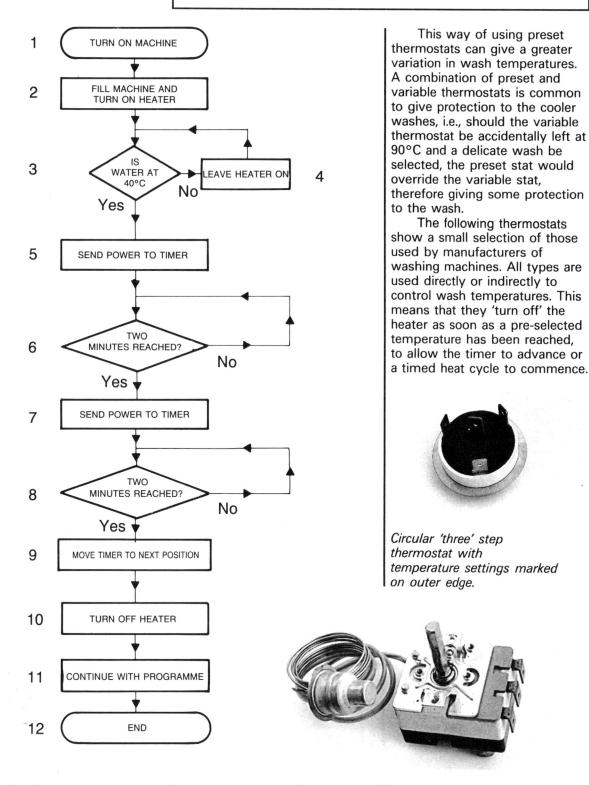

1. TURN ON MACHINE

2. FILL MACHINE AND TURN ON HEATER

3. IS WATER AT 40°C — No → 4. LEAVE HEATER ON

Yes ↓

5. SEND POWER TO TIMER

6. TWO MINUTES REACHED? — No

Yes ↓

7. SEND POWER TO TIMER

8. TWO MINUTES REACHED? — No

Yes ↓

9. MOVE TIMER TO NEXT POSITION

10. TURN OFF HEATER

11. CONTINUE WITH PROGRAMME

12. END

This way of using preset thermostats can give a greater variation in wash temperatures. A combination of preset and variable thermostats is common to give protection to the cooler washes, i.e., should the variable thermostat be accidentally left at 90°C and a delicate wash be selected, the preset stat would override the variable stat, therefore giving some protection to the wash.

The following thermostats show a small selection of those used by manufacturers of washing machines. All types are used directly or indirectly to control wash temperatures. This means that they 'turn off' the heater as soon as a pre-selected temperature has been reached, to allow the timer to advance or a timed heat cycle to commence.

Circular 'three' step thermostat with temperature settings marked on outer edge.

12 for the programme to continue as required. For the purpose of this flowchart, the wash will end here, as we are only concerned with the operation of the thermostat at this time.

Note: This is only used as an example to illustrate the use of the thermostat, and does not actually represent the way in which a wash is formed. For further information regarding the timer, see the chapter: *Timers (programmers).*

Variable thermostat showing the switches, capillary tube and pod.

Smaller two step thermostats, found on Zanussi, Fagor and Bendix, etc.

What is a thermistor?

A thermistor is a solid state device used in place of a fixed or variable thermostat. The thermistor's particular properties allow them to be used as infinitely variable temperature sensors that have no moving parts. They are also incapable of going out of calibration, i.e. giving incorrect temperature resistance values, but occasionally they can and do go 'open circuit', or connections to and from them may short circuit. Both are faults which will inevitably give rise to temperature sensing problems.

Where is it located?

Like all temperature sensing devices, it must come into direct or indirect contact with the substance (air/water) or the item that needs monitoring. Its location is therefore similar to the other themostats but methods of fixings will differ.

How does it work?

Unlike other temperature control devices the thermistor cannot

work alone. It is an electrical resistor, the resistance of which varies in relation to its temperature. There are two ways in which it varies depending on manufacturer, and the requirements of the finished product. Thermistors can be positive or negative temperature co-efficient. In simple terms, this means a positive co-efficient thermistor's resistance increases as its temperature increases and conversely, a negative co-efficient thermistor's resistance decreases as its temperature increases. Thermistors are therefore rated as P.T.C. or N.T.C. respectively. The N.T.C. type of thermistor is the version most often used in temperature sensing circuitry in automatic washing machines, e.g. Hoover, Servis, Hotpoint, etc., a theoretical operation of this is given below. It is essential that only the correct variation of

Typical solid state thermistor.

thermistor is used which conforms to the rating requirements of the machine and it circuitry.

The variation in resistance to temperature change forms part of an electronic circuit, the output of which controls the advancement of the selected wash programme, in either mechanically or electronically controlled machines. On electronically controlled machines, i.e. those without mechanical timers, the resistance of the thermistor is monitored directly by the main programme circuit board or sub module, see: *Timers (programme control)*. However, thermistors can be found on machines with mechanical timers/programmers and the way in which they work in this instance is as follows. The resistance of the thermistor forms part of a temperature control circuit. There may be a separate module solely for this purpose or it may form part of the motor control module as in some Hotpoint machines. A theoretical operation of such a system is given below.

In this instance the output voltage at D & C are used to control a triac (an electrical component within the circuit). The triac in turn switches the thermostop coil on a mechanical timer or impulse to control panel of a computer control machine. See: *Timers (programme control)*.

Being an electronic circuit in either mechanical or computer controlled machines, the operating voltage within this portion of circuit will be low (5 volts DC). Therefore, any electrical testing of the thermistor must be with a low voltage test meter as voltages of over 9 volts will damage the thermistor or module circuitry.

The two resistors Ra and Rb are of the same value. A 5v DC voltage supplied to point A will take one of two routes depending on the resistance opposing it, i.e. A.C.B. or A.D.B. Route A.C.B. has within it four

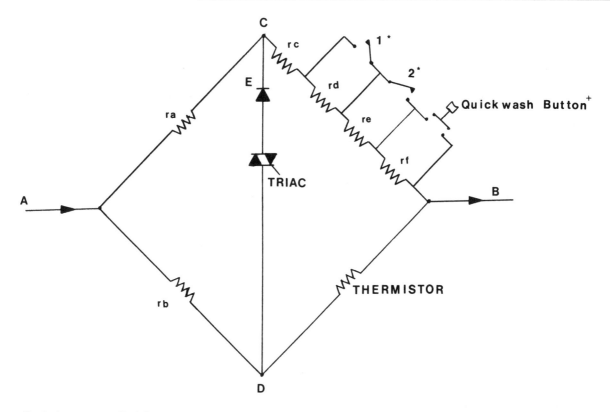

* = Switches controlled by timer wash selection. (These switches would be electronic not mechanical on computer controlled machines).

+ = Button on facia of machine which is a user selectable option.

resistors each of which can be switched in and out of the circuit in relation to the programme selected and temperature required for that wash cycle. The diode at point E eliminates reverse supply to the triac. The route A.D.C. contains the thermistor in its second leg D.B. If we assume that the water within the machine is cold, then the thermistor resistance will be high. This will allow a current from D to C thus energising the thermostop or holding the programme on the heat cycle until the predetermined temperature (governed by the switchable resistors) is attained. Releasing of the thermostop or

impulse of programme is as follows. As the water temperature increases, the resistance of the thermistor decreases (N.T.C.). At some point the resistance in both sides of the circuit will be equal and at this point, no current will flow between D & C and the triac will switch off. This in turn will release the thermostop on mechanical timers or allow impulse to the next stage of the programme on electronically controlled machines. Variations in temperature are gained by switching in or out the required resistors in the C.B. leg of the circuit, thus altering the point at which equilibrium is reached within the circuit. All switches open = all resistors in circuit RC + RD + RE + RF would result in high resistance, therefore a cooler wash of say 30°C is achieved. Quick wash switch closed = resistor RF bypassed, i.e. lower total resistance gives wash of say 40°C. Switch 1 closed = two resistors in circuit RC & RE may relate to 50°C with option of quick wash switch to further

reduce temperature (and time) if required by user. Switch 2 closed = three resistors RC, RD, RF in circuit may relate to 60°C with option of quick wash switch to further reduce temperature (and time) if required by user. All switches closed = this will leave only RC in circuit at this point, and a high temperature of say 90°C would be achieved, again with option if required.

Note: The option to alter the temperature selected by the set programme, i.e. by pressing a quick wash or short wash option button on the control panel, may be bypassed itself by the timer on some programmes. This means that although in the theoretical operation detailed above, each setting could be further affected by the quick wash switch, in reality, this may not be the case as a quick wash may not be suitable for certain types of wash loads.

T.O.C.s

The term T.O.C. is an abbreviation for thermal overload

cut-out. In simple terms, if the item the T.O.C. is attached to or is in proximity with gets too hot (over a predetermined temperature), the T.O.C. will operate and open circuit the supply. The way in which it works is very similar to the thermostat, both of which use the bimetal strip system. Thermostats are in fact used on some machines as T.O.C.s to open circuit for instance the heater if an overheat fault occurs. However, the term T.O.C. generally relates to the smaller devices that are embedded within or on top of motor winding coil of all types.

There are several variations in style and size, each of which being matched to its particular use and position within the appliance or apparatus. It is therefore essential that only the correct style and temperature rating is used when renewing a T.O.C. Those that are used to protect motors and pumps, etc., are rarely renewable and usually form part of the original winding or moulding. If a T.O.C. has gone open circuit, it will have done so for a particular reason therefore this safety item must not be bypassed. Always ensure that any replacement component contains a T.O.C. Some pattern spares may miss out this fundamental safety device in order to cut production costs so take note that such an omission could be unsafe.

Although designs and ratings of T.O.C.s vary, there are two basic types of operation; A. The self-setting T.O.C. This is like a thermostat and resets when a normal working temperature returns which may result in a cycling of the fault, i.e. the safety T.O.C., due to a fault open circuits the heater supply. This would result in the cooling of the heater and the water, in the process the T.O.C. also cools and in doing so returns power back to the heater.

The manual reset T.O.C.

The action of this type of T.O.C. is identical to that described above except for one main difference. Once tripped, it cannot reset itself and has to be reset manually usually by simply pressing a button or rod.
Note: This must be done with the machine isolated, i.e. unplugged, and only after the cause of the tripping has been eliminated.

Thermal fuses

Many appliances now have this type of overheat protection device. It can be found protecting the heater on certain makes of machines, especially those with plastic outer tubs such as the later Hotpoint and Servis machines. It is essentially a fail-safe device which when actuated by a predetermined temperature goes open circuit. Once open circuit, it cannot self set or be manually reset, therefore renewal of the thermal fuse is required once the device has gone open circuit. Renew the thermal fuse only when the fault which caused it to operate has been corrected, i.e. pressure switch system blockage allowing heater to energise without water in the machine.

It is a solid state device and as such contains no moving

parts or contacts that may in themselves fail. Thermal fuses alleviate the possibility of fault cycling, are cheap and in most instances easy to fit. They are small but easily recognisable and are often housed in protective sheaths or mouldings.

There is a wide variety of temperature ratings available to suit the various applications, so great care must be taken when replacing the device to match the original rating/item. Do not under any circumstances consider bypassing this device for any reason whatsoever.

Thermal fuse or micro temp as it is sometimes called. The device will often be housed in an insulated flexible sleeve.

Arrowed is the thermal fuse (overheat detector) used on Hotpoint machines with plastic outer tubs. It is housed in a tubular recess within the heater unit. Individual replacement parts are available.

Chapter 23

Suspension

During the normal washing and spin drying operations of front loading machines of all types, a great deal of vibration is produced. The level of vibration increases during the spin sequences, especially if the wash load is out of balance or severely under loaded. If the outer tub unit was fixed rigidly to the shell/outer casing of the machine, damage would be caused to both internal components and to the immediate location of the machine through excessive movement of the free-standing machine.

To avoid the transference of vibration produced during wash and spin cycles, the inner tub unit of front loading washing machines is supported within the shell/outer casing of the machine by vibration absorbing supports, i.e., suspension. Due to the confines of the shell/outer casing of the modern machine, a limited amount of movement is allowed, but any excessive vibration and movement of the tub unit is removed (damped) by the action of the suspension system supporting the unit.

Note: To prevent damage to components within the machine during transportation/deivery, some means of packing will be

fixed to the machine to stop any movement of the tub unit, i.e., rocking suspension. It is essential that any such packing or transit fixings (as they are commonly known) are removed. There are as many different types of transit packing as there are machines so read your instruction booklet for a description of how to remove the packing from your new machine. It is advisable to retain these instructions and packing should it become necessary to transport your washing machine again, e.g., moving house. If you

do need to refit the transit packing, a good idea is to put a sticker on the door reminding you that the machine must not be used until the packaging has been removed.

Remember, the suspension is the system that controls all of the movement of the tub unit when it is in use. Without the suspension or when it is damaged, the whole tub unit will move violently when in use. See also: *Out of balance detection* later in this chapter.

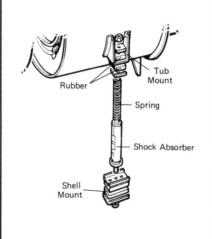

LARGE DAMPER & MOUNTS

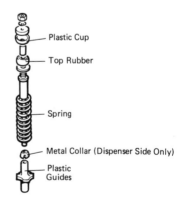

SPRING ONLY UNIT HOOVER TYPE

What different types of suspension are there?

The spring type suspension, which is simply large strong support springs (used only on early slow spin machines). Slide and spring damper – supporting the tub from beneath with only small springs or straps at the top for holding the tub unit in mid fore and aft position. The damper and spring suspension which is not unlike the system in motor cars. The friction damper, which consists of two arms gripping a metal plate tightly, therefore slowing down the movement of the tub.

Slide and damper types

The main faults to check for are those of guide wear, allowing the shaft to jump out of position, and also the top rubbers to soften or wear. This results in a phenomenon called 'twisted tub'. The reason for this is the suspension on one side of the tub is not correctly positioned, therefore allowing one side of the tub to bang on the side of the shell and cause damage. A noise fault can also become apparent at the top of the suspension due to soapy water seeping into the suspension via the dispenser or dispenser hose. This is best removed by a spray of lubricant/moisture repellant and an application of Molycote to the top bush and slides, The top and the guides of the suspension are the only parts that should be lubricated in this way.

When fitting top rubbers, the machine should be laid on its face, and the suspension should be held tightly with grips at the top end only. The top nut can then be undone. Do not hold the bottom of the shaft as any marks will quickly wear the plastic guides. When refitting, thoroughly clean the metal shaft and apply a smear of Molycote lubricant paste to the shaft and upper shaped washers. The plastic slides should also have the same paste applied prior to refitting.

The friction damper system

The friction damper system is not unlike the disc braking system on a motor car. Two support rubbers with asbestos (or similar material) pads are mounted on two spring steel arms. These rest either side of the flat plate attached to the outer tub. When the outer tub moves, the action is slowed down (damped) by the friction of the pads against the plate. This is a very cheap and very effective form of suspension.

When this type of damper is worn, the tub will move excessively and possibly emit a squeaking noise. The noise will be caused by the rubber pad mounts coming into contact with the moving plate, due to the friction material being worn. This is easily overcome by the renewal of the pads themselves. After isolating the machine it should be laid on its back or side to enable the steel spring arms to be opened. When opened, the pads can be prised from their ball and socket joint.

Note: If the pads on this system become glazed and/or shiny on their contact faces, a 'chattering sound' will be noticed. It may be possible to avoid renewal, by slightly roughening the faces with sandpaper to remove the glazing and then refit. If unsuccessful, the pads will have to be renewed. Do not under any circumstances put oil or grease on friction damper systems. Do not inhale the dust from the friction pads as they can be harmful to the lungs. Moisten with water during removal and cleaning to avoid airborne dust particles. Do not blow them clean. Dispose of old pads safely and wash hands after contact.

The damper and spring system

The damper type system is similar to the shock absorbers on your car, and they do the same

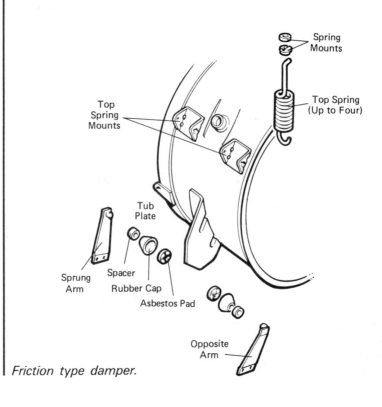

Friction type damper.

job. If the smaller version of the system is used, the tub will not actually rest on the damper, but will be hung from springs at the top of the tub, using the dampers at the bottom for shock absorption only. In the larger systems however, the tub is held only by much larger dampers at the bottom of the tub, with retaining straps/springs at the top to limit movement fore and aft.

Faults found with this type of solid damper will have the same symptoms as the friction damper system. The only remedy in this case is the complete renewal of the faulty damper. This can be done by laying the machine onto its face, taking the usual care and isolation procedures. Access to the dampers can be gained by removing the back panel, and unbolting the damper from the shell and tub mounts.

The spring only system

The spring only system may also be found. The spring or the

Indesit friction damper that shows the spring steel arms clearly. These support the rubber mounts with friction pad inserts.

A friction damper system from a Fagor machine. This is viewed in situ, as the complete front panel can be removed. The front panel removal can be achieved easily by removing the lower panel and two securing screws.

mounts can be changed separately if required or replaced as a complete unit. **Note**: The left and right springs of all systems are usually of different ratings. Be sure to specify the required side when obtaining a replacement. Also, where two small springs are used for fore and aft support during repair, it is possible that they may become dislodged. It is essential that they are refitted correctly. Please examine the correct positions and make notes of all springs, etc., before you start.

It must be stressed that any combination of these systems may be found. A damper system may complement a friction damper system. Please read all sections thoroughly before starting any repair on the suspension system.

The purpose of suspension in the automatic washing machine is to damp the oscillations of the spring mounted tub and drum unit. Counter-weights of concrete or in some instances iron, are used to help in the overall balance of the unit and to add weight to the appliance to further help in eliminating movement during use (especially spin). The suspension system works the hardest during the distribute (pre-spin) and spin

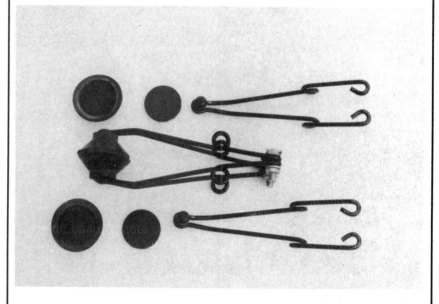

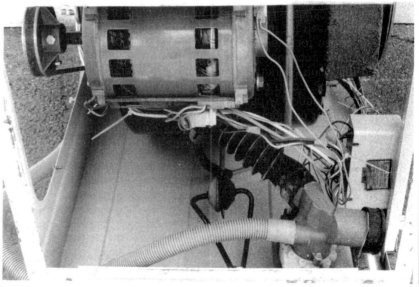

1. View of spring and slide suspension. This is prone to softening of the rubber mount at the top of the suspension leg.

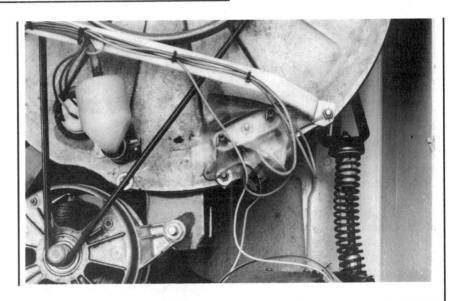

Note: If the top springs are removed, mark them so as to ensure that they are replaced in the same order. This is because the length and tension for the springs may differ for each position.

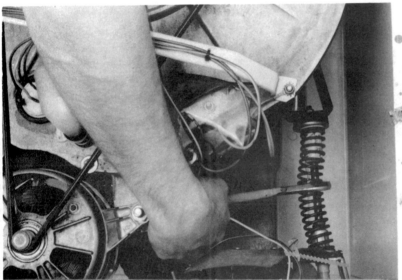

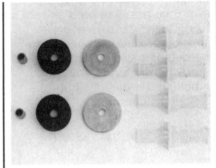

4. New set of rubber sleeves and spacer washers. Do not be tempted to renew one side only – you must renew both sides!

2. To renew the top rubber, the whole unit will have to be withdrawn. Grip the shaft through the spring at the top only, using adjustable pliers inserted through spring.

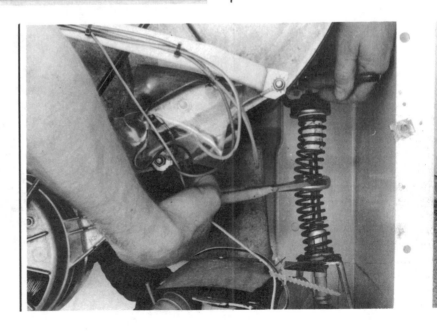

3. Whilst gripping the metal shaft tightly, the securing nut can be removed. (Right hand thread). Note the correct assembly of parts and pull spring downwards to remove top bush.

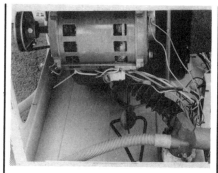

5. Friction style damper. Access is much easier with hoses removed. Do not lubricate this type of suspension.

6. Friction pads from various machines. Top section is pad and mount for Zanussi, middle section pad for Indesit, and lower is square pad for Candy.

cycles. Under normal load conditions the simple suspension and counter-weight system works well and reduces tub oscillation as long as all components and connections are secure and in good order. However, if severe out of balance occurs because of a mechanical fault, e.g., worn suspension, under loading; one bath mat, overloading; large duvet, or by washing unsuitable items, such as trainer shoes, excessive vibration and damage may result to both the outer cabinet and internal parts due to the suspension being unable to cope with such adverse oscillations of the tub unit within the confines of the shell/cabinet.

All but the earliest of front loading automatic machines have a pre-spin speed or distribute as it is often called, the action of which is to balance out the wash load by rotating it at a preset drum speed. The centrifugal force created by the pre-set speed (usually around 83rpm on the drum) arranges the wash load evenly over the inner surface of the drum prior to acceleration into the spin. However, this process can fail if:
1. A balled load occurs, i.e. the knotting together of items usually as a result of poor loading by bundling all items into the machine together instead of separately. Stopping the machine, removing and replacing the items individually is usually all that is required for this problem. **Note:** It is wise to reset the machine to a rinse position before the spin to allow correct distribution to take place.
2. Underloading occurs when insufficient clothes are in the drum to distribute evenly around the entire surface, i.e., half drum surface covered but other half not, thus giving a flywheel effect when rotated. **Note:** This is a common fault on some machines and aggravated by the user removing items in the hope of improving the matter when in fact extra items are required.
3. Overloading resulting in little or no free movement of the wash load therefore no distribute action is possible. This will also result in a poor wash.
4. An unsuitable wash load of, for instance, trainers, sleeping bags, etc., will create severe out of balance situations and subsequently damage to the machine and/or its surroundings. Try to load the machine correctly.

Out of balance protection

The best way to avoid out of balance problems is to load and use the machine correctly, although even having done this, an out of balance situation may still develop. Many modern machines, especially later computer controlled models now incorporate a means of detecting an out of balance situation and will take steps to rectify it by re-balancing the load by extending the distribute phase or by terminating the acceleration up to full spin speed thus limiting or avoiding further vibration or damage.

How does out of balance detection work?

O.O.B detection as it is known can be detected two ways:
A. Electro-mechanically – This method uses light-action microswitches strategically mounted on the edges of the outer tub or on the suspension legs. They may be actuated by a weight on the arm of the microswitch or by a contact bar, either of which will be adjustable for calibration of O.O.B. movement. The microswitch is linked into the motor speed module control circuit, see *Motors (speed control)*. Excessive movement or inertia resulting from an out of balance situation will actuate the microswitch at a predetermined level. The impulse caused by the microswitch's operation terminates the build up to the spin speed selected and normally allows only the distribute speed to operate. After a period of time governed by the circuitry of the module, a spin sequence will be reinstated in the expectation that a second distribute has cleared the O.O.B. problem. If this is not so, the process is repeated. With mechanical programme timers, this process may continue (dependent on the make and

model of the machine) until the time allotted for spin has elapsed. Computer controlled machines are often programmed (see: *Timers (programme control)* chapter, to accept only three O.O.B. impulses before terminating the spin or remainder of the programme completely. The setting of the mechanical O.O.B. detection micro switches differ greatly between the different makes and also between the different models from the same manufacturer, hence no specific adjustment details can be given within this text.

Chapter 24

Timers (Programme Control)

The programmer (or timer, as it is more commonly known), is the unit located at the top of the machine, directly behind the selector knob on mechanically controlled machines, whereas machines that are controlled electronically may have the programmers split into two or more circuit boards (modules as they are usually known).

When a programme is selected, the timer follows a pre-determined sequence switching components on and off (i.e., heater, pump, valves), for various lengths of time. Due to the apparent complexity of this component, it wrongly tends to be regarded as a 'no go' area.

The intention of this manual has been to show that the automatic washing machine is not so mysterious, and when broken down into its constituent parts, its simplicity of operation is revealed. To describe the workings of the timer in your particular machine would require the make, model number, date of manufacture and the timer number itself. These are needed to ascertain which variation of timer and associated variation of programmes that your particular machine has. In their most infinite wisdom, the

manufacturers have seen fit to change their timers, numbers and wiring colours, etc., with regularity.

For instance, the Hoover automatic in the last ten years has seen at least fourteen basic models in this time, but at least twenty six variations of timer and no less than thirty different wiring diagrams. The other manufacturers are no better. The story is much the same had we selected Hotpoint, Bendix or any other manufacturer, yet the machines' other internal parts have changed very little in that period. As you can see, to give detailed information about the unit that is in your particular machine, a book several times the size of this one would be needed. What follows is a general description of how timers work, some of the most common faults and their symptoms.

How an electro mechanical timer works

What follows is a description of how an electro mechanical timer works, in this instance a Crouzet timer. This is one of the most common timers and is found in

more than fifty per cent of the machines sold in Britain today. The Crouzet is an edge cam timer, which means that each switch within the timer is operated by its own cam on a central rotatable barrel. This allows several switches to be dropped or lifted into different positions at the same time. This operation can be likened to that of the old style piano or musical box that played a tune with the aid of a cylinder. If the cylinder were to be changed, a different tune would be produced. The same principle applies to the timer. Although the external appearance of the timer does not change, a simple change of the central barrel will give the manufacturer a different switching sequence and therefore a different machine to put on the market. Because of this, when changing the timer it is important that the correct version is used, i.e., one with the same central barrel. This is shown by the serial number on the timer.

On the central barrel there are several cams, with each cam having two corresponding switches. The barrel is rotated by the cam advance motor, which is energised by impulse commands such as that from the thermostat, i.e., if the selected temperature is reached, the thermostat closes, thus causing the timer motor to run. The motor will continue to run until a cam position is reached that breaks the impulse path (timer motor circuit). The barrel is now in the correct position for the next sequence of instructions.

The Crouzet can be found with 45 step cycles. This means that on one complete revolution of the cam, it will have initiated 45 separate positions (45 'clicks'). A more popular variation to this, is one of 60 step cycles. These are usually found when half of

Typical sectional. Crouzat timer.

the timer cycle is for robust washes and long spins, and the remaining section given to cooler washes and short/delicate spin, i.e., letters A–F on the selector knob for hot wash, rinse and long spin and G–K for delicate wash, rinse and short spin.

There are two distinct variations in the way the cam barrel is advanced: a) timers with two drive motors mounted on the rear and b) a single motor drive system. A description of both types is as follows:

Type a) this style of timer is easily recognisable by the two small drive motors mounted in the rear of the timer. Each has its own function, one of which is dedicated to cam advance as described in the previous

Crouzet timers have either a large code number on the top of the timer or a smaller, longer number on the left hand side. When ordering a new item all numbers that are on the timer should be quoted together with the make, model and serial number of your machine.

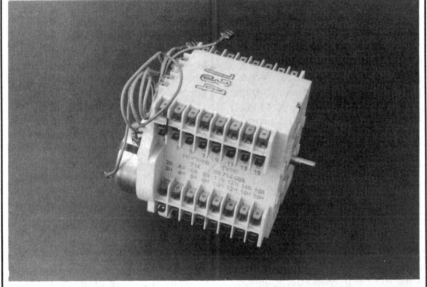

Typical face cam timer (terminals on rear).

Internal view of cam barrel. Each row is for one switch block and has three levels.

Internal view of switch bank. Note switch movements and cam position (Crouzet timer).

Bendix face cam (Eaton timer).

Indesit edge cam timer.

paragraph, and is called the cam advance motor.

Next to the advance motor is the timing motor, which times all of the functions of the machine, i.e., washing, spinning, etc. The timing motor drives a timing cam which, via internal gearing, turns for instance, one revolution every two minutes. Therefore a six minute wash consists of three, two minutes timing requests. The rotational times may differ depending on the requirements of the appliance manufacturer.

Another function of the timing motor is that it reverses the main motor on the wash action cycle. This is done by continually rotating two cams, on which two sets of switches are located. The combination of which are used depending on the type of wash selected. For instance, if a delicate wash is selected, the main wash motor receives power via the switches for five seconds (clockwise rotation), pause for fifteen seconds, then rotates for five seconds (anticlockwise). The cam does this by continuous rotation

Shown is one of the easiest types of timers to replace. This type has Duotine block connectors and not single tags. Some later edge cam timers may be able to accept block connectors instead of tags. This makes timer removal and refitting a great deal easier.

Timers with block connectors are much easier to fit. This timer has connections only on one side, a great improvement on its predecessor.

Shown are early and late Hoover timers. The timer on the left has individual connections for each wire, whilst the later timer on the right uses block connectors.

This timer uses both block connectors and single amp-tag fittings.

in one direction but lifting the switches into three separate positions, ON, OFF, ON (reverse feed to motor). Delicate and heavy washes can be achieved by using different configurations of the same sequence. A heavy wash for example could be made up of the following sequence: wash for fifteen seconds clockwise, pause for five seconds, and wash for fifteen seconds anticlockwise. The times of fifteen and five seconds are not random choices, but are directly proportional to the two minute timing cycle. The times of rotation and pause will differ between timer types and the requirements of the appliance manufacturer but will be proportional to the rotational time of the cam, e.g., 17, 3, 17, etc.

Switches resting on the main cam barrel controlled by the advance motor can also be moved into three positions by the cam they are resting on. For example, at the correct point in the programme, the cam on which the heater switch rests will allow the switch to make, therefore engaging the heater. The cam will also engage the correct thermostat switch for that programme. When the correct temperature is reached and the timer has timed out, the thermostat then impulses the cam advance motor. In English, this is read as 'When the temperature is reached, finish timing and then impulse (move) onto the next cam position'. This means that both functions of the motors can sometimes be interlinked.

Type b). The alternative to the two motor Crouzet, is the one motor version, where the one motor carries out both functions of timing and cam advance. This version is common in many current automatics. Timers with one motor for both timing and cam advancement fall into two further categories; the thermostop version and the temperature plus time version.

Single motor driven timers

One motor Crouzet type to fit Creda.

are required to give the same wash programmes as their two motor counterparts. The main wash motor action is again governed by an independent cam to the rear of the main cam barrel. When power is supplied to the timer motor, the cam rotates by internal gearing usually on either a 1 minute or sometimes 2 minute cycle depending on the make/type of timer. Once on every rotation a small 'pawl' located within the 'timing cam' (so called because of its known rotation time), locates with the main cam barrel and moves it on one cam position thus giving the progression through the programme cycle.

However, some washes require the use of the heater to increase the water temperature and in some situations needs a fair length of time to do so. If the programme barrel were to impulse, say, once every minute, it would move off the position that supplied power to the heater too quickly. Simply stopping the motor via a thermostat until the required temperature is attained would seem to be the answer, but in reality no wash action could take place as the timing cam upon which the wash action switching takes places would also stop. As mentioned previously, there are two ways of avoiding these drawbacks.

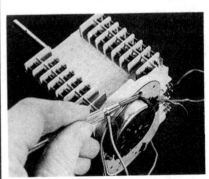

1. On many timers it is possible to renew the timer coil should a simple open circuit of the coil occur. First ease fixing clip latch.

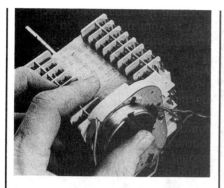

2. Slide clip sideways to free drive motor. Do not mix the motors if two are fitted as it is likely that each rotate in different directions.

3. With motor free of rear of timer, further strip-down can commence.

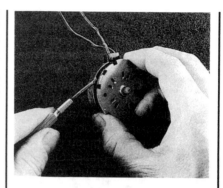

4. Carefully insert a small flat bladed screwdriver between the two halves of the motor and ease them apart at the three securing points.

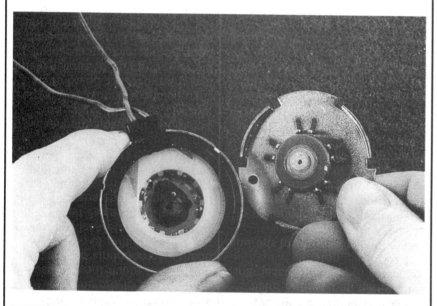

5. With care both halves will separate as shown.

6. The motor coil can now be lifted free of the casing.

7. Ensure that the new coil is correctly fitted (identically to the original) and that the small plastic anti-reverse cam is correctly positioned prior to re-assembly.

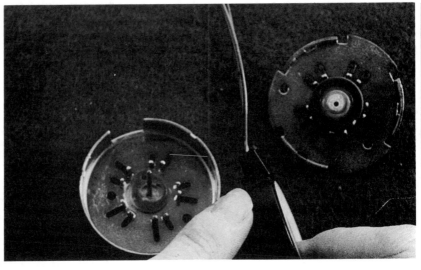

8. When all parts are in position press both halves of casing firmly together and ensure free rotation of shaft in one direction only (as original).

Refit to timer in reverse order making sure that the securing clip is tight. **Note**: Removal of the timer for this procedure is not normally required. It was removed in this instance for photographic purposes only.

Typical edge cam timer with thermostop system housed under rear black plastic cover.

A. Thermostop timers

To allow wash action to take place, i.e., rotation and counter rotation, during heating periods without impulsing the main cam barrel once every rotation of the timing cam, a solenoid (electromagnet) is used. The solenoid is located on the rear of the timer and when energised, pulls a metal plate on to the now magnetised metal core. This action mechanically lifts the timing cam pawl that would normally impulse the main barrel and, although the timing cam is free to rotate, the pawl is unable to locate and move the main barrel. The solenoid forms part of the thermostat circuit that relates to that particular wash programme. When the predetermined temperature is reached, the thermostat in series with the solenoid coil will go open circuit and sever the power to the coil. This in turn removes the mechanical retardation of the pawl which is then free to impulse the main cam barrel on its next rotation. This combination of thermostat and solenoid coil is most often referred to as a thermostop system for obvious reasons. **Note**: The thermostop coil may not be energised continuously throughout the heat cycle. Often it is actuated by a switch resting on the rotating timing cam to only engage (if required) each

Thermostop timer with rear cover removed to expose solenoid coil and lever mechanism.

This AKO timer is yet another version that uses a thermostop system.

time the pawl comes up to its impulse location point. If this did not occur, the coil may overheat. Testing of the coil is a simple test for a closed circuit, testing for cam action within the timer cannot be easily verified. Confirm all other functions before suspecting internal mechanical timer failure.

B. Temperature plus time

This type of single motor timer does not use mechanical retardation of the timing cam pawl. The operation of this type of unit uses a fixed temperature thermostat as a reference point upon which a series of timed heat cycles will commence. A

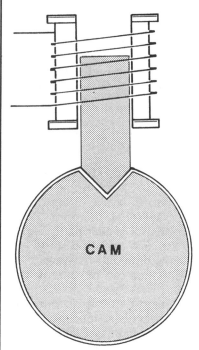

Diagram A. Shows the theoretical action of the thermostop, the action of which prevents cam advancement until the thermostop coil is energized, i.e., thermostat closes when correct temperature is reached.

simulated wash may be as follows. A wash of 40°C is selected by the user. The inlet valves, governed by the main cam barrel selects a cold fill only of around 12°C commences, and when full to the correct level, the pressure switch will transfer power from the valve to the heater, see *Water level control* chapter. Static heating will take place until 30°C is reached, i.e., no wash motor action due to the timer motor being supplied via 30°C normally open (N.O.) thermostat. The water temperature will soon rise and close the 30° thermostat in turn completing the timing motor circuit. The timing cam is now free to rotate and impulse the main cam barrel. The next

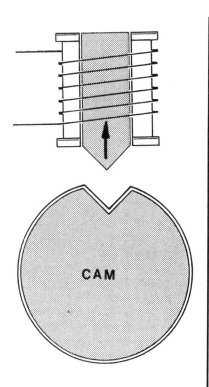

*Diagram B. Shows thermostop coil energized i.e., thermostat closed (temperature reached) thus allowing the main cam barrel to advance. **Note:** The action of a thermostop system may also be the opposite of this sequence, that is to say locked when energized free to advance when not. In such instances normally open thermostats would be used and a matching timer programme.*

impulse would put into circuit the wash motor, and combined with the rotation of the timer and cam create wash rotation and counter rotation. The timer now also has a reference temperature of 30°. Normally water in a machine rises 2°C for every one minute of heating, therefore the next five cam positions would leave the heater in circuit thus attaining a 40° wash temperature via a 30°C thermostat, i.e., temperature plus time. Controlling the type of fill (cold, mixed or hot only) along with a sequence of cam positions with the heater in circuit, a wide range of temperature variations can be achieved. In reality, a combination of fixed and variable thermostats are often used. The fixed thermostats giving set wash temperatures and the variable thermostats allowing the user to select their own setting if required (only on certain programmes). To avoid the selection of a temperature that is too high, the fixed thermostats usually override any incorrect setting of the variable thermostat. This usually allows the variable thermostat control over robust wash programme settings or cooler than normal selections for other programmes.

With a little imagination, it should be quite clear how a programme actually works, not by some mysterious phenomenon, but by a sequence of simple movements that combine to form a complete operational programme.

How a face cam timer works

The same basic principles apply, only the switches are operated by an etched disc that allows the switches to drop in and out of the recessed positions on its face. Face cam timers are of the one motor variety as described above.

The timers are readily identifiable by the fact that an edge cam timer is much longer or deeper than the face cam. This is because the face cam timer is much slimmer due to the fact that only one disc is used to operate all of the switches.

The main drawbacks of timers.
(a) Units cannot be repaired. Complete unit changes are needed for internal timer faults. However, on some timers, drive motor coils can be renewed if simple open circuit has occured,

see: *Using a meter* chapter.
(b) Without detailed information of the switching sequences of the faulty timer, internal faults are difficult to trace.
(c) Units can often be difficult to fit (unless a logical approach is used!)

The main benefits of timers.
(a) Modern timers are very reliable.
(b) New units can be relatively low in cost, although this differs from make to make of appliance. Having said that, the price variations for similar parts (e.g. only the cam barrel on some makes is different) between some brands can be extremely wide.

It must be remembered that when a fault is suspected, it is not always the most complicated component that can cause the most trouble. If a process of elimination is used and all other parts of the machine are found to be working correctly, it is only then that the timer should be suspected. (Unless of course in the case of obvious failure, such as a burn out or damage to the timer.)

Note: Ensure that the power is turned off and that the plug is removed from its socket at all times. Do not remove the timer from the machine at this point.

The removal and subsequent exchange of the timer can be a long and tedious task on some machines, and should not be undertaken lightly. However, several of the more modern machines have improved the way in which the wiring harness is fitted to the timer. Multi block connectors are now used on many machines making timer renewal much easier. Do not fall into the trap of replacing the timer because of the ease of the job. Correct diagnosis of the fault and a methodical approach to both fault finding and perhaps subsequent replacement of the timer is essential.

Do not remove any wiring as yet, but thoroughly check for any overheating of the connections to and from the timer spades

Types of timer internal switches.

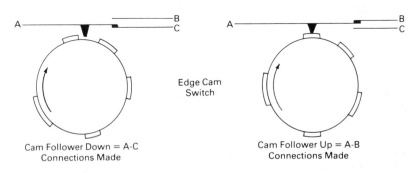

Edge Cam Switch

Cam Follower Down = A-C
Connections Made

Cam Follower Up = A-B
Connections Made

Edge Cam Switch Action.

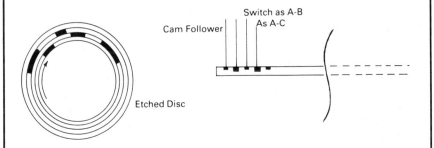

Cam Follower

Switch as A-B
As A-C

Etched Disc

Face cam timer.

(connections), i.e., if a fault is suspected in the heater switch, trace the wire from the heater to the timer. This gives the location of the heater switch and should be examined for any signs of burning or being loose. This would at least confirm your suspicions.

Having decided that the timer is at fault, a note should be taken of all of the numbers that are on the timer, together with the make, model, serial number and age of your machine.

Timers (programmers)

Armed with this information, you can obtain an exact replacement. When the replacement has been obtained, visually check that they are identical, as timers will not be exchanged by any known company, once they have been fitted. (You have been warned!) Having confirmed that it is the correct replacement, and any accompanying documents have been read thoroughly, you can proceed to swap the wiring. The only way that this can be done is by placing the new timer in the same plane as the original, swapping the wires or block connectors on a one-to-one basis. Although very time consuming, this is by far the safest method. A mistake at this point would be almost impossible to rectify without a wiring and timer diagram, therefore it is advisable to ask a colleague to supervise operations. When all connections have been successfully exchanged, the timer can be fitted into position, ensuring that any parts that are connected to door interlocks, etc., are positioned correctly, then double check the work carried out and earth continuity. Once fitted into position, and the covers have been refitted, the power can be turned on, and a functional test programme can be implemented. **Note:** Some timers have small metal clips that join/link terminals

together. These generally do not come with the new timer. Ensure they are swapped from the original.

Timer variations

The timers shown are a small selection that are used in today's automatic machines.

A manufacturer may have numerous variations of the same timer. For instance, although your timer may be a Crouzet, your neighbour may have the same machine with seemingly the same timer in it, but in fact, it may be a variation of the same timer. These variations are identifiable by the slight difference in serial numbers shown on the timer. This illustrates the need to obtain the exact number of your timer and machine when a replacement is to be obtained.

Some machines have pushbuttons only to select the required programme and or a selector knob. The switch/button bank usually consists of an 'on/off' button, a series of selector buttons for various wash types and combinations, and a start button. Alternatively, a rotatable selector knob or wheel may be used in conjunction with a start button. On these types of machines, the timer is of a similiar type to those described earlier and can be of the face or edge cam version.

The buttons/selector act as bypasses to unwanted sections of the programme, for instance, the selection of a pre-wash cycle will allow the timer to advance to that position missing out all the steps before and after it when the start button is pressed. Sometimes a combination of switches can be used but all act as 'impulse' or 'by-pass' depending on the length and type of wash required by the user. In reality, the buttons select the required programme in place of the user manually turning the timer shaft via the programme knob.

Computer controlled machines (electronic timers)

The functional parts of these machines, i.e., motor, drum, pump, etc., differ little from machines with conventional selector knobs and mechanical timers. Microprocessor controlled machines are easily recognizable by their digital displays used to indicate the programme in use and buttons or touch pads for programme selection. Most have the ability to display an error code when faults occur which relate to a table in the handbook. Faults within microprocessor timer circuitry can be difficult to locate as the complex circuitry board components cannot be easily checked. It is best to eliminate all other possible causes of faults before suspecting either the power module or programme unit. If all the other checks prove satisfactory, then check all connections to and from the control boards (microprocessor machines generally have two – one low voltage board for the micro processor, selector panel and display, and one power board with transformer, relays and thyristors to operate the mains voltage switching which the processor cannot do directly). The connections to printed circuit boards are prone to oxidization giving poor electrical contact especially on the low voltages used by the programme boards. Check closely for poor connections.

If the fault remains after all other components have been checked and found to be satisfactory, the only option left is to change one or other (or in some instances, both) of the circuit boards. Due to the way in which the power board functions (see following paragraph), it is most likely to be a failure in this circuitry or its components at fault. Do not touch the processor board's components at all as they are sensitive to static electricity and are easily damaged by careless handling. The power boards are more robust but care must still be exercised when handling them.

The power board is generally much bulkier than the programme board and houses a large transformer to drop the voltage to the processor. Electronic circuit faults occur more often with power boards as the mains switching operating the pump, heater, etc., is switched mechanically by relays or electronically by thyristors operated by the lower voltage supplied from the programme board, i.e., processors themselves cannot directly switch mains power and use mechanical relays or thyristors. Try to isolate if a mechanical fault is suspected (e.g. heater not receiving power, maybe a sticking/faulty relay, etc.)

Items that short circuit and blow fuses may also damage their control relay or thyristor. For instance, a simple fault such as the live supply to the outlet pump breaking loose during a spin cycle and touching the

Control and power boards from a typical computer controlled washing machine.

Front facia of a computer controlled machine with control board removed. DO NOT touch any board components. See note on static prevention. Handle such boards only by the edges.

Internal view of computer controlled machine with control board clearly visible behind front facia of the machine. This particular machine does not use ribbon cable for the connections that lead down to the power module housed at the base of the machine.

earthed metal shell of the machine would result in a direct short circuit. Such a fault on a machine with a mechanical timer would blow the appliance fuse in the socket and rectification would be straightforward. However, the same fault on a microprocessor controlled machine is likely to damage the components of the circuit board used to switch the pump supply, resulting in a much more expensive repair.

The programme board may also be referred to as the display board or module. It differs from the power module in that it is much slimmer (but often much wider) than the power board and lacks the larger components such as relays, transformers, etc.

It is usually mounted behind the front facia of the machine although variations in positioning will be found between manufacturers and models within each range.

This large power board was damaged by a simple fault (short circuit of pump connections). However the damage caused to the power board due to the simple short circuit resulted in a complete new board being fitted.

Ribbon cable is often used for the connections between the control and power modules. The one shown is from a Servis machine.

Obtaining individual components from the machine manufacturers is not possible as only complete boards/modules are supplied as spares. The control microprocessor is normally located within the circuitry of the board but may, on some machines, be included within the power board circuitry. As explained earlier, the microprocessor takes the place of the cam barrel used in mechanical timers. The mechanical action of the cam barrel of physically switching components on or off is now carried out electronically by the solid state processor, i.e., no moving parts (although moving part relays may be required elsewhere), and the timing of each sequence is governed by a quartz clock chip, similar to that used in watches, within the board's circuitry.

The way in which the processor operates is very similar to the cam barrel in that it is programmed with unalterable predetermined functions, i.e., steps. The main difference is that the amount of steps can be (and usually are) much greater and the response from external sources (feedback) can be utilized to monitor the processes being carried out, for instance to check the time of fill automatically, power consumption of motor, etc. Like

the mechanical barrel, a predetermined set of functions are stored within the main chip in a similar way to the individual cam positions of the mechanical timer. The main difference being that a greater amount of 'positions' can be stored and accessed in any order unlike the fixed sequence of the mechanical version. The way in which a full wash programme is compiled is by electronically overriding or omitting the sequences not required. In this way an extremely variable and flexible wash programme can be built up with information obtained from the various wash selection buttons operated by the user and combined with fixed sequences to suit the type of washload.

The various wash options finally selected by the user and then held in volatile memory, i.e., held short term only for as long as the machine is switched on, but will be lost when turned off. **Note:** Some degree of memory retention is incorporated (approx 5-10 seconds) and varies from make to make. Most machines also have a set sequence of wash programmes plus the ability to store several user defined variations in a volatile memory that will only blank if the machine is unplugged for a period of time.

Faults within the

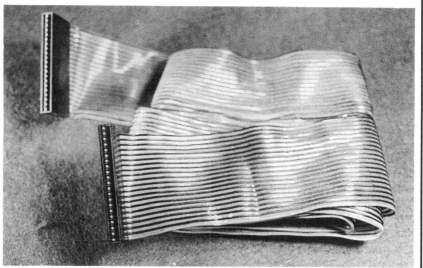

components or circuitry of the board are extremely difficult to trace and as with the power board, only complete units are supplied by the manufacturer. Before contemplating a board fault, ensure all other components within the machine are satisfactory and that all connections to and from the printed circuit boards are in good condition and are firmly pushed into place. Check thoroughly all connections, wiring and all protective covers. With the machine isolated, look closely at all connections that carry mains voltage when in use, as loose connections can cause over-heating and interference which can affect the processor chips. Include all earth path connections in the wiring checks and renew any that are loose, have cracked covers or show signs of damage, for example, overheating. Do not forget to include the plug connections.

With a persistent or unusual fault, i.e., intermittent operation, random displays, works for short periods and then blanks memory, etc., check the condition of the supply socket. If a poor connection exists between any pin of the plug and its supply connection, again interference will be present which may corrupt the processor, see *Basics – electrical*. Renew if suspect.

A faulty suppression unit may also be the cause of such random and difficult to trace faults. Ensure the unit is securely earthed, see *Suppressors* chapter.

With the need to prevent interference from particular components within the machine, items such as the main wash motor, may have small suppression units called chokes, see *Suppressors* chapter, which prevent any interference being transmitted along the wiring of the machine. Ensure that any chokes fitted within the machine are secure and in good condition (e.g., check continuity). If all the aforementioned checks prove satisfactory, then it is most likely

that the processor chip is corrupted or the board has a fault within its circuitry. Such faults will require a replacement unit. Carefully note all connections to and from the unit and keeping in mind the paragraph regarding handling of the unit, remove it from the machine. Inspect it closely for dirt or debris which may be affecting the circuit or its components. If any dirt is present, it should be blown free (do not use metal items such as screwdrivers). Check the board for cracks or possible moisture damage due to faulty covers, etc. Before finally accepting that a new unit is needed, it would be wise to inspect the printed circuit board's soldered connections to verify that they are sound, i.e., loose or poor connections (called dry joints) can often be easily rectified. If all these checks prove negative, a new unit will be necessary. Take care to fit the unit correctly on all its mounts and ensure all covers and connections are

When testing for continuity of the ribbon cable only, insert a metal plate in one end to make contact with all connections as shown. Use a low voltage continuity tester to confirm continuity of each wire. Ensure the cable is moved during the test so as not to miss an intermittent fault.

sound. Take particular care to avoid direct contact with the components of the unit.

Do not touch the processor board's components at all as they are sensitive to static electricity and are easily damaged by careless handling. The power boards are more robust but care must still be exercised when handling them.

Note: All checks must be carried out with the machine isolated in the usual manner – taps off, plug out! Under no circumstances should you try to test the processor board even with a low 9 volt or similar tester because the microprocessor chip can easily be damaged. Use of the 1.5 volt tester shown in the photograph is recommended for continuity testing of the wiring between the module units. Try to leave the block connectors in place and using the probes of the tester, check for continuity between exposed printed circuit points close to the connector blocks. This will test both the wiring between the modules (usually ribbon cable) and the connection to the printed circuit board.

On computer controlled machines the faults that develop may be indicated by a code which is displayed on the front of the machine. Codes differ from machine to machine so refer to your handbook to ascertain the meaning of each code.

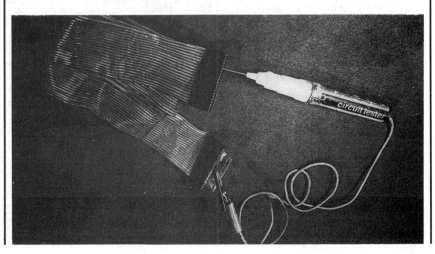

Chapter 25

Low insulation

What is low insulation?

Low insulation is best described as a slight leak to earth of electricity from the wiring of one or more of the components or wiring in an earthed appliance. If very slight, this will not harm the appliance but is an indication of faults to come and should be corrected immediately for safety reasons.

What does it do?

Low insulation is a gradual breakdown of the insulating properties of a normally electrically leakproof system, which will eventually result in a short circuit to earth if the root cause is left unattended.

How is it caused?

This can be caused by normal wear and tear over a long period, resulting in a breakdown of the insulating coating on wiring, motor windings, heater elements, etc. Such a breakdown of insulation may not result in a failure of the part at this point and the appliance may still function as normal. However, this is no excuse to ignore low insulation as failure to trace and rectify low insulation is both foolhardy and in the long run can be costly in both money terms, and above all safety. Faults such as leaking/weeping shaft seals can give rise to water penetrating the motor windings and resulting in low insulation. If not corrected, this could lead to a complete failure of the motor, or worse. A simple renewal of the shaft seal and careful cleaning and drying of the T.O.C. and windings may be all that is needed to save money and improve safety for all concerned. It is important not to compromise on safety by ignoring such symptoms.

How can it be detected?

When an engineer tests for low insulation, he will use an instrument called a metrohm/low insulation tester. The law requires repair engineers to test for low insulation, and there is a low minimum allowable level. The law stipulates that the following tests are made by commercial repair engineers.

Between the earth pin on the plug and all earth connection points within the appliance, the maximum resistance should be 1 ohm, i.e., very low resistance – a perfect connection.

With the appliance turned on, but unplugged, test between the live pin on the plug and the earth pin on the plug. The minimum resistance should be 1 megohm (1 million ohms), ideally no detectable reading, i.e., very high resistance — no connection at all. Repeat this test between the neutral and the earth pins of the plug.

Testing of internal components can be carried out easily by removing connections to the part and connecting one lead to one of the free terminals and one to the earth terminal and testing, minimum resistance – 1 megohm, then repeat using the other connection.

These tests are carried out using a meter designed to test insulation by applying a high voltage (500 v) at a very low current for safety to test the insulation quality of the part to which it is connected. It is an unfortunate fact that many engineers do not possess such a device, and therefore do not check for low insulation. This does not mean that you should not!

A meter to test for low

insulation would cost upwards of one hundred pounds and is therefore out of the reach of most D.I.Y. people. An alternative is to utilise an in line circuit breaker (see flowchart). The appliance is plugged into the circuit breaker, which is then plugged into the socket, unless an R.C.D. already protects the circuit or socket. As mentioned in *Basics – Electrical* the purpose of the device is to detect low insulation or leakage to earth and turn off the power to the appliance. Although this is not the ideal way of testing for low insulation, it will help in locating it and provide safety for the appliance and its user.

It is wise to test R.C.D. systems on a regular basis to ensure they function correctly and are fully operational when needed. Follow the instructions shown on the unit or on the leaflet accompanying the adaptor. If a fault with the unit is suspected it will need to be tested and possibly re-calibrated for maximum performance by a skilled electrician using a special R.C.D. test meter. If a fault is suspected in an R.C.D. unit, have it checked as they are there for your safety.

The use of an R.C.D. in this way is to aid those who do not possess a low insulation test meter. If must be remembered that the units have a wide range of uses and cannot only be used in this manner. R.C.D.s are designed to ensure safety when using appliances or equipment such as lawn mowers (where there is a danger of cutting through the cable), irons, washing machines, etc. (where water and electricity are in close proximity).

If any appliance trips an R.C.D. (or similar) systems, do not use the appliance until the fault has been rectified. If tripping occurs with no appliances or load on the system, then a fault on the house wiring is indicated and the trip switch should not be reset

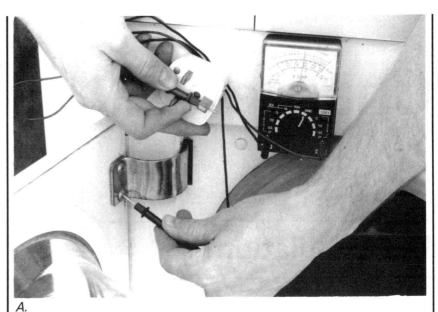

A.

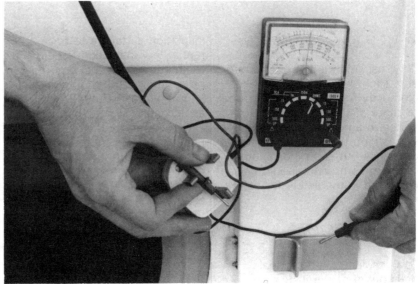

B.

Testing for earth using an ammeter. Note that in Picture A, the door hinge is used, and in picture B, the metal door slide is used in this instance.

until the fault is found and corrected.

Have your R.C.D. tested regularly by an approved electrician or Electricity Board to ensure that it functions correctly and safely at the right speed of no more than 0.4 of a second. Such tests require an R.C.D. test meter that calculates the trip

time of the unit. On simple tests the unit may trip but take too long for it to be classified as safe.

Points to remember about low insulation

Ensure that any disconnection or removal of wires is safe and not earthing via another wire or the metal case of the appliance, etc.

Whilst disconnecting any wires during the testing for low insulation it should be remembered that the machine must be isolated from the mains at all times and the panels or covers must be replaced before the appliance is re-tested, i.e. **Do not test with exposed wiring**.

Before testing for low insulation, using a circuit breaker all earth paths of the appliance should be tested. This is done by connecting a meter between the earth pin of the plug, and all other metal parts of the appliance in turn. Maximum resistance should be 1 ohm. See chapter *Using a meter*.

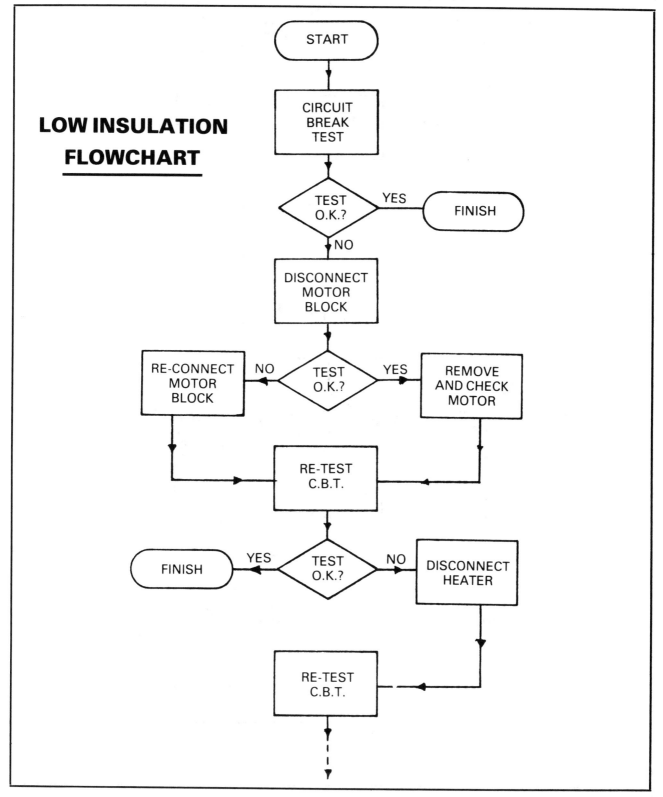

LOW INSULATION FLOWCHART

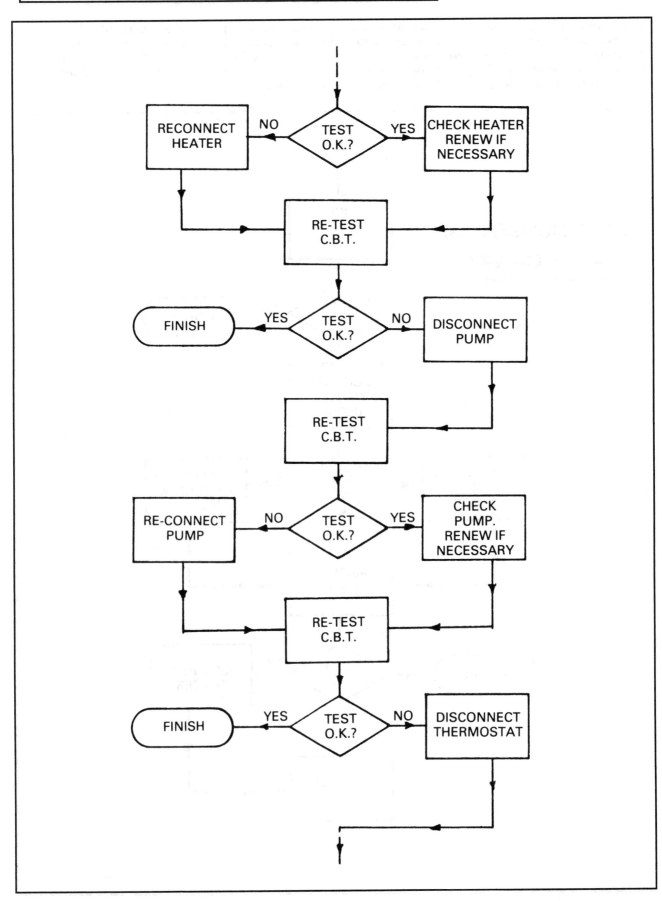

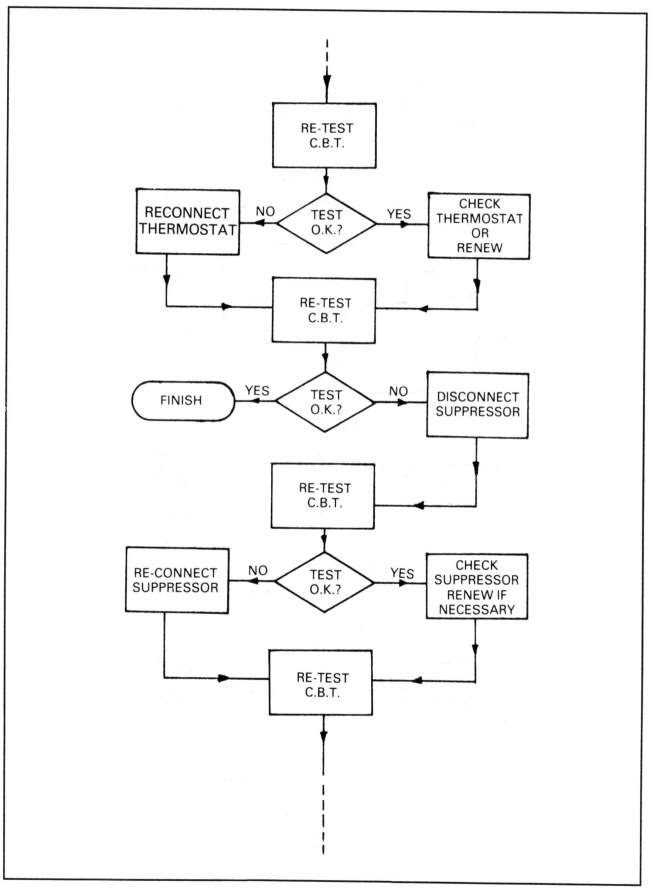

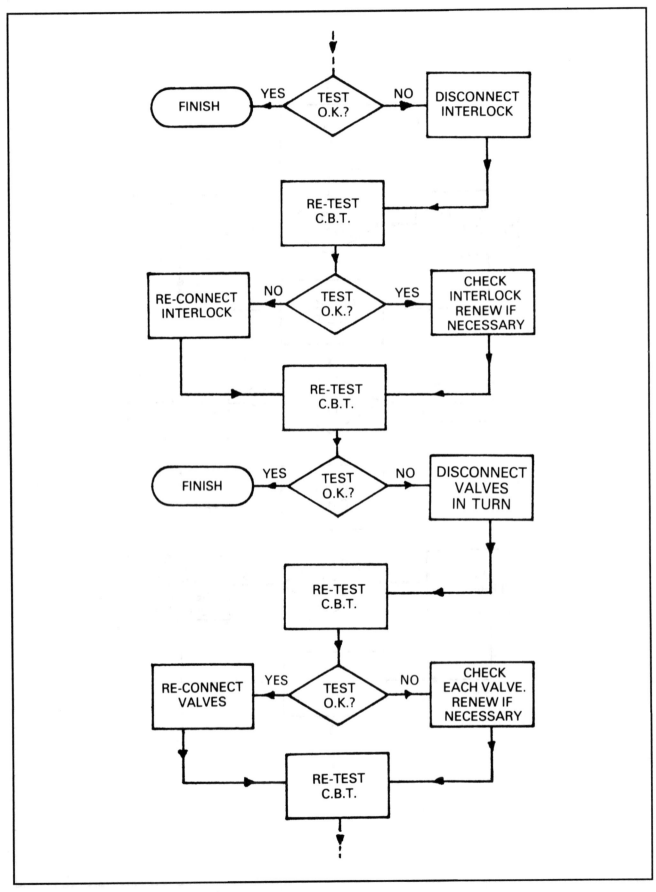

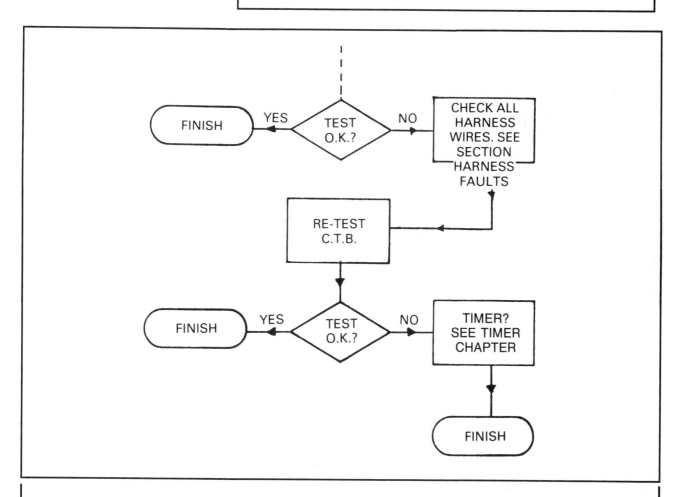

FINISH ← YES ← TEST O.K.? → NO → CHECK ALL HARNESS WIRES. SEE SECTION HARNESS FAULTS

RE-TEST C.T.B.

FINISH ← YES ← TEST O.K.? → NO → TIMER? SEE TIMER CHAPTER

FINISH

Two popular RCD adaptors. An essential item for all households that do not have RCD protected supply circuits or socket outlets see Basics – Electrical chapter.

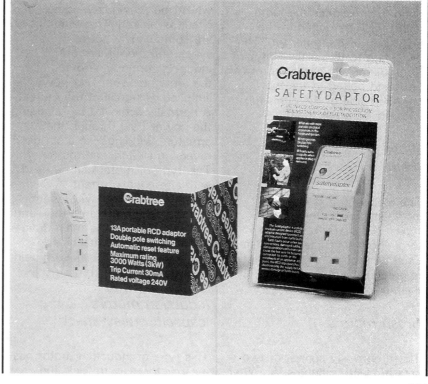

Chapter 26

Motors

There are three types of main wash motor used in today's machines, the univeral A.C. brush motor, permanent magnet (P.M.) D.C. brush motor and induction motor.

Where is the main motor located?

On most machines the motor will usually be bolted to the underside of the outer tub. The exception to this is the Hotpoint front loader where the motor can be found bolted to the top left-hand side of the outer tub (viewed from the rear).

What types of motor are there?

The following text is a brief introduction into the various types of motors found in use throughout machines in general. Each type of motor is described in greater detail later in the chapter.

Brush motors

These normally consist of two sets of electromagnets. An outer fixed set called the field coil, and an inner set free to rotate called the armature. The armature is made up of many separate windings and is configured in such a way that power is only supplied to one set of windings at a time. The corresponding movement induced in the armature, continuously brings a new set of windings into circuit, whilst the previous winding circuit is broken. The windings are continuously out of synchronization, therefore inducing continuous rotation of the armature whenever power is supplied. Reversal of the motor is normally achieved by reversing the power flow through the armature windings via a set of reversing switches in the timer. This type of motor can be used with alternating current (A.C.) from the mains, or with direct current (D.C.) from a battery, and is often used for the main drive motor in washing machines, especially on machines with spin speed above 1000 rpm.

Induction motors (capacitor/relay start)

This type of induction motor has a capacitor/relay to 'kick' the rotor into action by putting a delay into the motor's start windings. The resulting imbalance creates rotation in the direction of the run winding current flow. A reversal of power in the run winding reverses the motor. Speed is governed by the amount of windings supplied with power.

Induction motors (shaded pole)

This type of motor is associated with pumps. It has a low starting torque, i.e., this style of motor is impeded from starting easily, as the initial rotation is only from copper segments bound into the stator. When power is applied to the stator coil, the copper segments create a permanent imbalance in the magnetic field produced. This induces rotational movement.

Induction motors (permanent magnet rotor)

This extremely simple style of motor is used to drive all versions of mechanical timers, both for timing and cam advance. Consisting only of a wound circular coil fixed around a permanent magnet rotor and supported at both ends by simple sleeve bearings, this motor can be made extremely small and at a low cost. As with all induction motors, its simplicity of construction limits it for use to A.C. supply only. A larger version of this principle is now being used to power outlet pumps in many modern machines. The P.M. motor is housed within a sealed plastic chamber but is still free to rotate by the alternating current (A.C.) supplied to two externally mounted stator poles. The rotor drives the impeller of the pump in the normal way, only the motor of the pump differs.

Brush motors in greater detail

A brush motor can be readily identified by its shape, as its length is normally greater than its width. Owing to their continuous switching device the commutator, the brush motor can be used either with A/C from the mains or D/C from a battery. The switching device (the commutator), is made up of many copper segments. Each segment is connected to a winding in the armature and is supplied with electricity through two stationary pieces of graphite, called brushes. These are pushed onto the commutator by springs.

When power is applied to the motor, current flows to the field coil and through the brushes to the commutator. This magnetises both the field and armature coils, inducing rotation due to the magnetic fields in both items being slightly offset from one another. As the armature moves to align the magnetic forces created, the next two segments of the commutator come into contact with the brushes as the first set go open circuit. This operation is repeated many times per second for as long as power is supplied to both parts.

Speed control of this type of motor is achieved by 'pulsing' within the speed control module circuitry varying the voltage supplied to the motor, i.e., if the pulse is slowed, the motor slows or vice versa. This is not as straightforward as it may seem, as the pulse has to be in the form of a lower voltage and smooth enough to eliminate any jerky action at low speeds. Full control is achieved by timer switch selection in conjunction

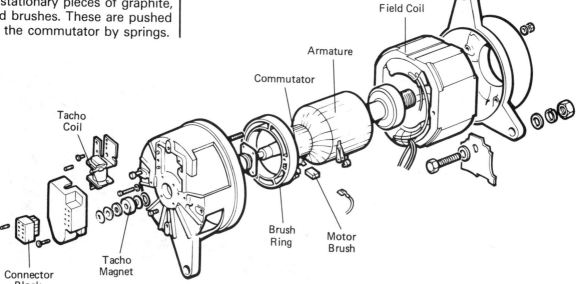

Field Coil

Armature

Commutator

Tacho Coil

Brush Ring

Motor Brush

Tacho Magnet

Connector Block

Shown is a typical Hoover motor. Many variations of this motor are currently available and are very similar. The motors look identical in every respect, except for the block connector at the rear. Although they look similar it is essential that you obtain the correct replacement unit for your machine. This motor is fully repairable and each component is available separately. Versions of this motor can be found on early Servis machines. When obtaining replacement parts or replacement motors, ensure that you always give the make, model and serial number of your machine.

with the speed control module which is dealt with in the section: *Module control in brush motors.*

Main drawbacks of brush motors.
(a) Generally noisy in use, especially at high spin speeds.
(b) Brush wear.
(c) Commutator wear/burning. Two or more segments incorrectly linking together. This would cause sparking and over-heating, resulting in poor running and eventual failure.
(d) Complete unit change needed if fault is other than brushes. This is true of most makes except for early Hoover where most parts are available separately.
(e) Prone to low insulation due to carbon dust created by brush wear.

Main benefits of brush motors.
(a) In general, much cheaper than induction motors.
(b) Infinitely variable speed control available.
(c) Small in size.

Brush motor armature change

The main aim of this photographic sequence is to show the removal of the motor from the machine, and the detailed removal and refitting of a new armature and brush ring. The motor shown is of a universal type to be found in many models of the Hoover range. It must be remembered that any connections that are to be removed should be noted to ensure their correct replacement at the end of the repair.

Also shown is the brush replacement for the G.E.C. type motor. Variations of which can be found in many machines such as Creda, Hotpoint and early Indesit.
Note: Any other fault with this type of motor requires a complete change of unit as explained earlier.

Armature change – Hoover type motor

1. Isolate the machine and remove the rear panel.

2. In this case a 'low insulation test' disclosed the motor fault. Remove the motor bolts and withdraw from the machine.

3. After noting the motor block colours, positions and connections, remove the plastic cover to reveal the tacho coil.

4. The tacho coil and magnet can be removed carefully. (The clip on the shaft can be lifted with a small screwdriver).

5. The four end rivets can be drilled out or removed with a sharp chisel, as in this instance.

6. Mark the position of the end frames, by marking with a pencil. When marked, remove the four securing bolts.

7. When the end bolts are removed, use a hide mallet (or similar) to free and remove the front end frame.

8. Knock the armature tacho end shaft free. Remove armature and inspect for faults.

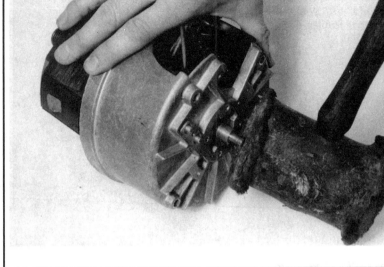

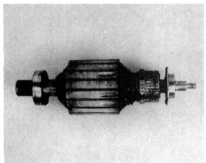

9. Check copper segments on armature for damage, i.e., burnt looking or loose/raised segments, and for carbon build-up. (This one is badly damaged).

10. Check the bearings for free and quiet running by spinning them on the shaft. Also check for tight fit to shaft. (This one had damaged the shaft).

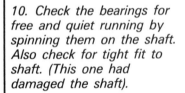

11. New armature ready to fit. Note screw plates and screws instead of rivets to aid fitting. Fit replacement unit if in any doubt as to condition of old unit.

12. Old brush ring inspected for damage. Carefully check for smooth brush slides. Also check that no carbon deposits have caused low insulation. Change if in any doubt. (This one has burnt slides).

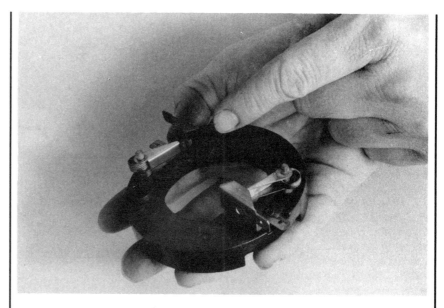

13. Fitting of new brush ring. If original unit cracked or damaged due to bad brushes, replace this unit. Slides should be smooth.

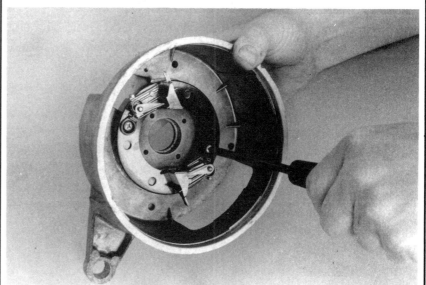

14. Shown are new and old brushes. The top lines show tagged and non-tagged type of brushes. The lower lines show split and worn brushes.

15. New armature fitted to rear end frame.

16. Hold plate on inside of end frame with finger. Insert and tighten the securing screws.

19. Refit front end frame and re-assemble motor, lining up the marks made in step 6.

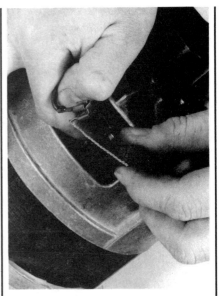

20. Fitting of new brushes. Ensure free movement of brush in slide. Make sure all connections are tight and do not foul metal body of motor.

17. Refit tacho magnet and clip. Ensure that when fitted the magnet will not turn on the shaft, i.e., it should be locked to the armature.

21. Ensure insulation strip is fitted to brush opening. It will fit easily if warmed first. The motor is now ready to fit to the machine for functional testing when all panels have been refitted.

18. Adjust tacho setting (if necessary). Screw centre up to the magnet and turn back $1\frac{1}{2}$ turns only.

GEC type motor (fault example)

1. GEC type motor. Early type can now have similar armature change as Hoover type, but generally only brushes fitted.

2. Removal of brush and holder from GEC type motor. Insert srewdriver and lift tongue of plastic at base of holder.

4. View of new brush and holder complete. Early screw-on type brush holders have separate brushes as above.

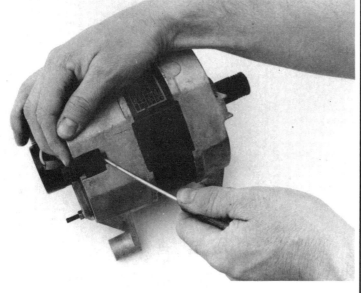

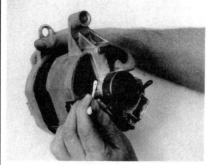

5. Ensure that any carbon dust deposits inside motor casing and armature are removed. (Blow out dust and clean with pipe cleaner or similar). Take care, do not inhale the dust.

3. Slide out brush holder complete with brush. Note length of new brush and check for good movement of brush in slide. This brush has worn very short.

6. Refitting of GEC type brush holder and complete brush assembly. Slide back into position carefully ensuring that tongue of holder engages into position.

Indesit type motor (fault example)

1. View of Indesit type motor showing similarity to GEC type motor which was fitted to earlier Indesit washers. This motor replaces GEC versions.

2. Main differences are the length of mounting arms and style of brush gear.

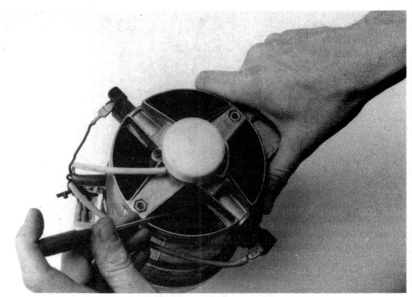

3. Brush holders are available as a spare part. Remove by pushing plastic locking tabs and pulling out holder. Pattern armatures can also be obtained for this style of motor.

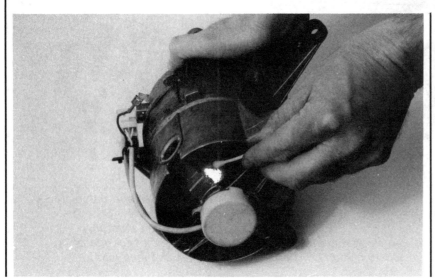

4. Ensure that any carbon dust deposits inside motor casing and armature are removed. (Blow out dust and clean with pipe cleaner or similar). Take care, do not inhale the dust.

5. Cause of this motor fault was a sticking brush in the brush holder. New brush and holder cured the fault.

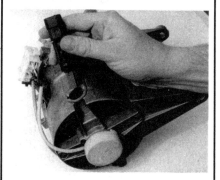

6. Refit new holder and complete brush assembly, taking care not to break or damage carbon brushes.

Permanent magnet (P.M.) motors

An unusual but reliable motor may be found on some appliances (mainly Philips), which is called a permanent magnet motor or P.M. motor for short. It is an extremely compact and versatile motor and due to its construction, runs on D.C. (direct current) only.

Permanent magnet motor (DC).
A. Motor casing
B. Ferroxdure magnet
C. Magnetic pole
D. Wound armature
E. Commutator
F. Drive shaft
G. Front bearing
H. Rear bearing

How does the D.C. (P.M.) motor work?

The D.C. motor, as the name implies, runs only on direct current (as opposed to normal household A.C. alternating

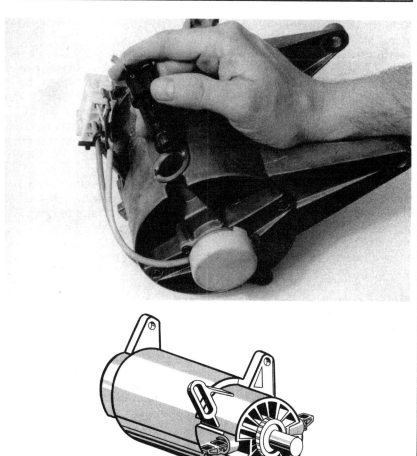

A P.M. motor.

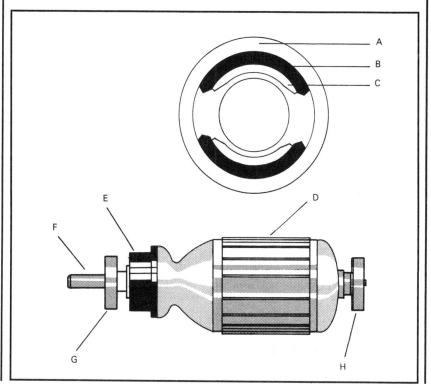

current). The operation of the motor is similar to the brush gear motor described in the previous section. D.C. power is supplied to a wound armature via a commutator and carbon brush system. However, there is no corresponding wound field coil. The motor has a permanent magnet field requiring no electricial supply, see diagram on previous page. Power (D.C.) is supplied only to the brushes. This induces rotation of the armature within the permanent magnet poles. Such motors are easily reversed by simply reversing the supply voltage to the brushes. Care, therefore must be taken when dismantling the appliance because if the terminals are accidentally reversed, the motor will run in the wrong direction during the distribute cycle causing severe problems. As always make notes when stripping down the appliance for repair or inspection.

Why are they used?

This type of motor is used because it is much smaller in size, lower power consumption, greater reliability, smooth running and low cost. Failure, other than brush wear, requires complete motor renewal – make sure only the correct replacement is obtained.

How does it get D.C. when appliance receives only A.C.?

Within the motor speed module there is mounted a bridge rectifier, see diagram below. A.C. power supplied to the module is rectified (changed) to D.C. voltage and supplied to the P.M. motor. The D.C. voltage supplied to such a motor induces rotation. The speed of rotation is directly proportional to the voltage supplied, i.e., the lower the voltage the slower the motor

turns, conversely, the higher the voltage the higher the motor speed. By using resistors within the module (and often a variable potentiometer mounted on the facia as a spin speed control) the motor can have infinite speed control. In practice, during wash action, i.e., slow rotation, the module via resistors controlled by timer switching may only be supplied with 16 volts D.C. but due to its efficient design and operation, it works extremely well and has good torque. During spinning, the D.C. voltage supplied to it can be as high as 250 volts D.C. No extra tacho system is required as the motor itself is an excellent generator of power. When running free the back E.M.F. can be used as a reference voltage for the module circuit.
Note: When using a test meter on the motor (checking for continuity/worn or sticking bushes), do not rotate the drum pulley or the motor quickly as the voltage generated may damage your meter. Remember all tests are to be carried out only when the machine has been isolated. On no account test for supply voltages to the motor. The voltages quoted do not represent those that may be found and are given only to emphasise the flexibility and operation of this type of motor.

Main benefits

Easily reversible. Small and compact in design. Extremely versatile. Cheap.

Full-wave bridge rectifier (both halves of wave rectified).

Drawbacks

Only motor brushes can be renewed, see photos.
The need to control the P.M. motor via a resistive circuit led to some machines within the range using a section of the heater as a motor circuit resistor. This system can be easily detected by a dual wash heating element being fitted. Therefore, when investigating problems with motor speeds on such machines, the element should also be checked. **Note:** It is the smaller of the two elements that is used but a fault with either will require the fitting of a new complete unit.

Module control for brush motors

It must be remembered that all motor speed faults are not directly attributable to the motor. The fault could be caused by a piece of electronics called a module which is connected between the timer and the motor and controls the speed of the motor. There is no standard location for the module but it is easily identified by its distinct printed circuit board (P.C.B.) and large heatsink. Computer controlled machines normally integrate the speed control into the power module, see *Timers (programme control)*.

How does it work?

The module obtains electrical information from both the timer and the motor. If the timer requires a wash speed it supplies power to the motor via the module whilst simultaneously

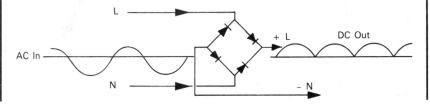

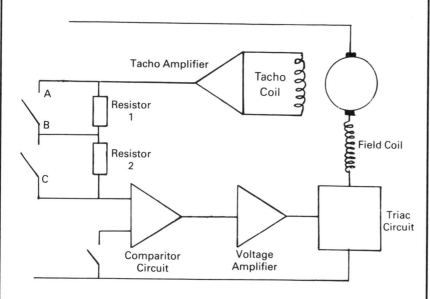

How to check if the module is at fault

If any of the internal components of the module have burned out, i.e., charred or burnt looking, the motor should be checked for any shorting, loose wires or low resistance, as these may be the probable cause.

Checks on the tacho magnet and tacho coil

(a) If the magnet is loose or broken, this would result in incorrect speeds at lower motor speeds.
(b) Severe damage or complete loss of the magnet would cause the motor to spin on all positions.
(c) A break in the coil would result in a spin on all positions. This is because a 'good' coil is usually about 200 to 1600 ohms resistance. If there is a break in the coil, the resistance is 0 ohms. The tacho generator is not returning any current, therefore the module speeds the motor up. The increased speed is not transmitted back to the module, so the process is repeated ad infinitum.
Note: Most modules fitted to modern machines have an inbuilt tacho test circuit and will not operate if the tacho circuit is open.
(d) Breaks and/or poor connections of the wires leading to and from the tacho can have the same effect. This is especially true at the connection block with the motor, and the connection at the module.

It should be remembered that any loose connection will be aggravated by the movement of the tub on the suspension, and this should be taken into account when testing for such faults. The following chart can be used to help locate the module faults and show the correct course of action. Do not attempt to adjust

switching in an appropriate resistor circuit in the module. There are two resistors in the example shown, therefore three speeds can be achieved, i.e., no resistors, one resistor, both resistors.

Wash speed – A, B and B, C closed: therefore bypassing both resistors.

Distribute speed – A, B open, B, C closed: therefore one resistor in circuit.

Spin speed – A, B and B, C open: therefore both resistors are in circuit.
Note: Some machines have a means of varying the spin speeds via a control knob on the front of the machine. This is simply a potentiometer (variable resistance). The inclusion of the potentiometer in the circuit will vary the switching of the triac over a wider range than the fixed resistors. Some machines have an off position on the switch, see *Machine will not empty* chapter.

The circuit of the module interrupts the power supply and varies the voltage supplied to the motor which in turn varies the motor speed. By pulsing components within the module at varying rates, the motor will either slow down or speed up.

On the rear end of the motor's armature is a circular magnet that revolves in unison with it.

Close to this magnet is a coil of copper wire (this may be encased in plastic), which is called a tacho generator. If a magnet is rotated next to, or inside a coil of wire a current is produced which is proportional to the rotational speed of the magnet. Therefore, the faster the motor is running the more current is produced. This current is fed to the module as a reference voltage and is used to monitor the performance of the motor by comparing the relative speed of the motor with a known voltage via the comparitor circuit. If the reference voltage is found to be lower than the comparitor voltage, the module will increase the pulse rate, therefore increasing the speed of the motor. If the voltage is found to be high, the pulses are slowed, therefore descreasing the motor's speed. This happens many times a second, and is undetectable. The diagram shown should help in understanding this principle.
Warning: The machine must be isolated from the mains. Turn off at the wall socket and remove the plug.

Washing Machine Manual

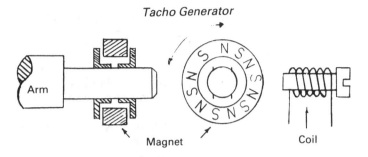

Tacho Generator

Arm · Magnet · Coil

Tacho generator

the tachometer other than as shown in the armature section.

The modules on the facing page are a small selection of modules that are fitted to today's machines. Their appearance and function differ very little from one another but are strictly non-interchangeable. Always ensure that the correct replacement unit is obtained by quoting the make, model and serial number of your machine when ordering spare parts.

If the fault persists the module is probably at fault. This should be replaced with a new unit, ensuring that the correct

The top left-hand terminal of this module shows signs of overheating/burnout. Loose connections can cause such problems but in this instance a poor soldered joint on the printed circuit board was to blame.

type is purchased. To fit, make a note of the connections, remove them and replace them on the new unit. It is important that the 'Duotine' (edge) connector fits tightly on the module (the connections can be closed slightly by inserting a small

screwdriver between the back of the tag and the plastic Duotine. Care should be taken not to close it too far as this may result in the tag not making contact by being pushed back into the connector).

The machine must be isolated from the mains. Turn off at the wall socket and remove the plug.

Warning: The large metal back of the module is used as a heatsink. This means that it is live when in use, and therefore should be fitted correctly and securely to its plastic mounts. Even when testing, any contact with the earthed shell of the machine will render the unit useless.

Incorrect Drum Action	Check Operation		Interlock	Motor	Tacho	Module		Tacho	Timer
			Check Interlock and Latch	Check Complete Motor Circuits	Check Circuit Late M/C's	Fit New One	Replace Original	Fit New One or Adjust	Check Timer moves on at all
	Spin	None	●	●	●	●			
		Slow		●		●			
		Cont		●	●	●			●
	Distribute	Cont							●
		None	●	●	●	●			
		Fast			●	●	●	●	
		Slow		●	●	●	●	●	
	Tumble	None	●	●	●	●			
		Fast			●	●	●	●	
		Slow		●	●	●	●	●	
		Cont							●

Hoover A/C (800)

Early Philips

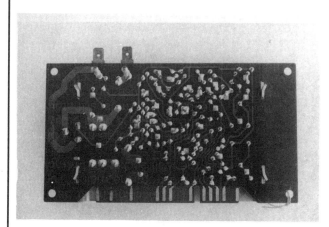

Creda A/C.

Hoover 1100.

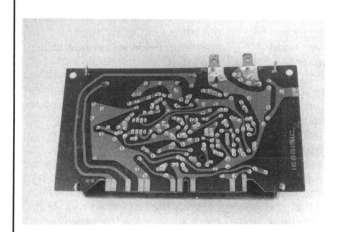

Servis A/C.

Hotpoint A/C.

Shown is the module from a Hotpoint Automatic. Note the discoloration that has occured on the centre of the PCB (front). This is a sure sign that the module is at fault or will fault soon. The reverse side of the PCB with the heat sink removed to show the components of the module clearly. The faulty components can be seen directly behind the area of discoloration. The component (a resistor in this case), has been overheating and subsequently failed. Repairs to modules are not merely a simple replacement of obvious components, as micro-chips within the circuit may have been damaged. We therefore advise that the module be removed and replaced with a complete new unit.

The induction motor

Most people seem to understand a little about universal motors (motors that require a wound armature and brush gear, etc.) but very little about induction motors or any type.

The asynchronous induction motor is in fact quite simple and uses the absolute basic principles of electricity. Its apparent complexity stems from the need to use extra windings to control its speed. Although modern electronics have allowed for variable control, we deal here with the basics to asynchronous induction motors and those used without module control. For speed control, see later paragraph.

Induction motors (capacitor/relay start)

Unlike brush motors, induction motors can only operate on alternating current (a/c mains),

and are technically called asychronous induction motors.

Single phase induction motors consist of two main items, an outer wound coil called a stator (see diagram) and a rotatable core called the rotor, made of high grade cast aluminium with internal metal laminations which are slightly askewed to aid torque for starting purposes (see diagram 2, page 129). The rotor is isolated from the windings and receives no power at all.

The most simple stator would consist of two sets of windings 180 degrees to one

another (see diagram 1). Two windings are needed to induce the rotor to turn by their magnetic fields when power is applied. One coil would not induce movement, though if the rotor were started by mechanical means, it would continue to turn as long as power was being supplied to the stator coil. In reality, the motion/starting is induced by placing one set of the windings 90 degrees out of phase with the other. This can be with the use of a relay, but more usually by the use of a capacitor, the rating of which is matched to the windings and is given in microfarads (µF) on its casing. Being out of phase due to the delay caused by the capacitor/relay, a rotating magnetic field is created, causing the rotor to turn up to speed at which point the start windings, as they are known, could be switched out if required. Reversal of the motor is quite simply a reversal of current flow through the start winding or the run winding, but not both. Speed reduction is obtained by the use of more wound poles of the stator being employed (see diagrams 1a and 1b, page 129).

When a motor, supplied with 240 v at 50 Hz (i.e. mains voltage) a 2 pole motor mimics the phase cycle and rotates at 50 revolutions per second, i.e. 50 x 60 secs = 3000 rpm, 4 poles 1500 rpm, 8 poles 750 rpm, 16 poles 375 rpm, variable speeds resulting in complex stator windings and expensive motors. Ensure that faults with motors are checked and rectified promptly. A loose motor block connection may allow power to one winding only and cause over heating and failure of the whole motor. A faulty capacitor or a malfunction of the programme switches or internal T.O.C. of the motor can also have the same result.

Main drawbacks of induction motors

(a) As all of the work is done by a complicated set of windings in the stator, this motor is generally not repairable and must be changed for a new unit.
(b) Capacitor failure often results in the motor failing to run. This can result in burn out as the rest of the motor windings are receiving power but no rotation

Module as used for induction motor speed control. (Control voltage applied to the motor to give smoother operation and variable spin speeds.

is possible. Overheat is inevitable, even when T.O.C. (thermal overload cut-out) protected.

Main benefits of induction motors – capacitor/relay start

(a) Generally reliable.
(b) Quiet.
(c) Can be run in both directions.

Warning: When checking for faults, the machine must always be isolated from the mains. Turn off at the wall socket and remove the plug. The capacitor(s) will still contain a charge although the mains has been isolated. This must be

discharged by using an electrically isolated screwdriver. Do this by 'shorting' the terminals of the capacitor with the shaft of the screwdriver ensuring that you are only in contact with the insulated handle. **It is not safe to proceed further until this has been done.**

If the stator windings of an induction motor are faulty, it may continue to run although appearing sluggish and getting extremely hot even when used for a short time. Therefore, if you

Typical capacitor for use with induction motors. Do not confuse capacitors with suppression units. They may look similar, but their functions differ.

Large Bendix induction motor, giving 400/800 spin facility. Smaller versions can also be found on later machines. A new addition to this range is the module control induction motor, similar to the Fagor version (shown later).

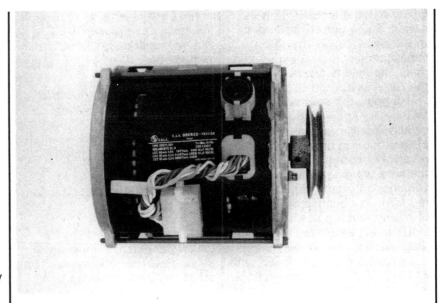

have been running the machine to determine the fault, proceed with care as the motor will remain hot for some time. If the motor appears to be very hot, the motor winding may be faulty and the unit should be replaced.

Module control induction motors

Many modern machines that use induction motors now use electronics to help control the selected speed more precisely and help smooth the transition from one speed to another. They differ little from their predecessors and still require a complex set of windings within the stator to give a series of fixed speeds. However, they do have the addition of further speed control via a speed control module and tacho coil and magnet arrangement which is similar to the system used to control brush motors.

The module works by ramping (slowly increasing) the voltage to the preselected (by the timer) stator windings. This achieves a smooth operation of the main motor. The tacho magnet and coil produce a small voltage proportional to the rotational speed of the motor which is used as a reference to the electronic module. This simply means that speeds can be increased gradually, for instance, allowing a slow build up to spin from distribute. This minimises the jump in speeds as the windings are simply switched in and out causing the

excessive vibration normally associated with early induction motors.

Ramping in this way allow the clothes in the drum to balance out more evenly by centrifugal force, resulting in a much smoother spin and less vibration of the machine. Another benefit of the electronic speed control is that a small potentiometer linked to the module and fitted to the facia panel of the machine enables the user to vary the spin speed to their own desired level (usually between 500–1000 rpm, with a switch facility on the potentiometer for no spin at all).

Faults in either motor or module would require a complete change as no internal components are available, except for the tacho coil. For faults and symptoms, see *Motors (module control brush motors)*.

The capacitor

What does a capacitor look like? Capacitors used for motor starting can have either metal or plastic outer casings with an insulated top with two terminals, see photo (page 127).

How does it work?

What follow is a simplified version of what happens within a capacitor in an A.C. circuit.

The two terminals of the capacitor are in fact completely insulated from one another. Internally they are connected to two sheets of metal foil and between this foil is an insulator. This package of large surface area is rolled into a tube formation which fits into the shell of the capacitor. If the two terminals and their connected sheets of foil are insulated from one another, you may ask, how do they pass a current when in use? The answer is that as the voltage supplied to one terminal is in fact alternating (i.e. at 50 times per second 50 Hz) so does the polarity of its connected foil. An opposite movement of electrons is produced in the other foil even though they are insulated electrically. This effect causes a delay in the electrical parth at this point, and this, in the case of an asynchronous induction motor gives the out of phase feed to the start winding.

The storage capacity of a capacitor is measured in microfarads (μF) and is displayed on the casing of the capacitor. Any replacement must be of the same μF rating.

If the motor fails to run on wash, but runs on spin and there are two capacitors fitted, it is possible that one of them is faulty. Change the capacitor with the lowest µF rating and re-test. If only one capacitor is fitted then the motor should be checked, see *Motors* chapter.

If the motor runs on wash but fails on spin and there are two capacitors fitted, there are two possible faults. Change the capacitor with the highest µF rating and re-test, remembering the previous warning about an isolated capacitor retaining an electrical charge. If the door interlock is connected directly to the motorspin circuit, and the door is not closed properly, then the spin will be prevented from operating. A fault within the interlock would also prevent the spin, refer to *Door switches (interlocks)* chapter.

The relay

What is a relay? A relay is an electro mechanical device used in this particular instance for induction motor starting in place of a capacitor.

What does it look like?

The most common relay consists of a plastic moulding with three terminal tags, two at the top and one at its base. On the centre section is a wire would coil (see photo).

How does it work?

The main aim of the relay in the context of asynchronous induction motors is to cause a delay in the start winding supply, similar to the capacitor. The main difference is that the relay achieves this operation mechanically. The wound coil section is connected in series with the run winding. When power is supplied to the motor, the current to the run winding

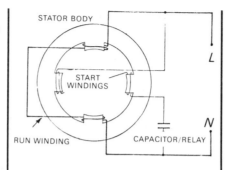

DIAGRAM 1

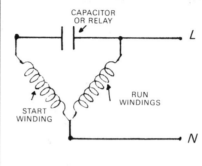

DIAGRAM 2

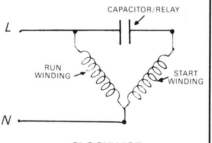

ANTICLOCKWISE
DIAGRAM 1A

CLOCKWISE
DIAGRAM 1B

passes through the coil and on to the motor run winding. This current induces a magnetic force in the coil which in turn attracts the metal core of the relay. The metal core is linked to an internal contact switch and when 'made' allows current to pass to the start winding (see diagram 3).This

operation gives the required delay to induce starting of the induction motor.

When power is switched off, gravity resets the relay core. It is, therefore, essential that the relay is in its correct position and the machine upright for this item to function correctly.

The relay may also be matched to the run winding of the motor, i.e., as initial power draw is high, the magnetic attraction of the relay coil is great enough to attract the core, but when the motor is running, the initial high power draw drops

A relay may be placed in circuit to cause the phase displacement necessary to start the induction motor. This is a mechanical delay as described and it is essential that the relay is upright when energized.

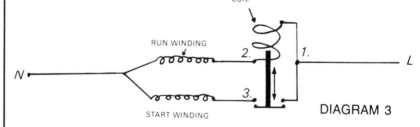

DIAGRAM 3

and weakens the magnetic pull of the coil. The core drops and open circuits the start winding allowing the motor to continue running more efficiently. Always make sure that the correct replacement is obtained by quoting model numbers and manufacturer when ordering.

Typical Relay.

Faults to watch for are: open circuit of the coil, metal core sticking (in either position), and contact points failing. Renew any suspect relay immediately as the failure of this item, like the capacitor, can lead to motor failure.

If you have to renew a damaged stator coil or motor and it is relay started, it is wise to change the relay at the same time as it may (a) have caused the original motor fault or (b) have been subsequently damaged by the motor failure.

The shaded pole induction motor

The shaded pole motor is one of the most simple of all induction motors and is similar in basic format of rotor and stator (see diagram). However, only one stator coil is used to create the magnetic field. Obviously this alone would not induce rotation of the rotor, only a constant magnetic field. To start rotation, an imbalance in the magnetic field is required which is done quite simply by copper band inserts at the pole ends of the stator laminations. The copper bands within the mild steel stator laminations (dissimilar metals) distort the magnetic field in a given direction, therefore inducing rotation in the stator. Reversing the supply to such motors does not effect any change in motor direction as this is governed by the direction of the fixed shaded poles. These motors do not have a high starting torque and because of

the magnetic imbalance being fixed, heating of the stator occurs which, under normal conditions creates no problems, but most stator coils are protected by T.O.C.s for safety.

Main drawbacks of induction motors (shaded pole)

(a) Can be used in one direction only. This is governed by the positioning of the shaded pole.
(b) Due to the permanent imbalance described previously,

excessive heat would result if used for long periods.
(c) Low starting power.
(d) If subjected to overheating for long periods, the motor will eventually fail, even if T.O.C. protected.
(e) Generally not repairable.

Main benefits of induction motors (shaded pole)

(a) Very cheap.
(b) Very reliable.
(c) Very quiet.

SHADED POLES

STATOR BODY

ROTOR

STATOR COIL

NOTE: CONNECTIONS CAN BE REVERSED BUT DIRECTION OF ROTATION REMAINS THE SAME. IT IS GOVERNED BY THE SHADED POLES ONLY

L

N

Shaded pole diagram. Note: Connection can be reversed but direction of rotation remains the same. It is governed by the shaded poles only.

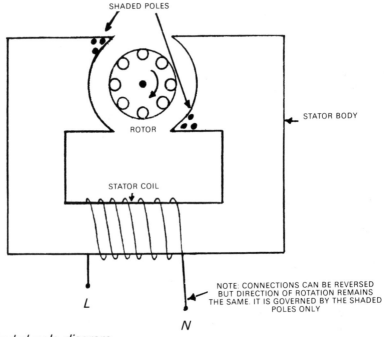

Bearing

Cooling Fan

Rotor

Stator

T.O.C.

Seal

Impeller

Pump Chamber

Typical shaded pole induction motor pump.

Note: T.O.C. = Thermal Overload Cutout.

This means that if the safe working temperature is exceeded, this device will sever the power supply to the motor. Most T.O.C.s are now self re-setting, resulting in constant heating up and cooling down of the motor. If the fault is not spotted quickly, the T.O.C. itself will fail, resulting in complete motor failure.

Induction motor – permanent magnet rotors

This type of motor has been used for many years to power the timing and advance mechanism of washing machine programme. As mentioned previously, some versions are now used to drive the outlet pump of some machines. It is the most simple of electric motors, quiet to run and cheap to produce. It also avoids some of the more common pump problems.

A circular multi-pole permanent magnet forms the rotor of the motor and its construction is similar to that described in the module control section relating to the tacho. Within the casing of timer motors a finely wound coil encased in plastic surrounds the permanent magnet rotor. Permanent magnet pumps have two coils wound on to a laminated steel stator (see photo). In both instances, supplying A/C power to the coil(s) induces rotation of the magnetic rotor. However, rotation could start in either direction and this, in the case of timer motors, would be most unwelcome. To ensure that rotation occurs in the required direction, i.e., clockwise or

Motors with permanent magnet rotors have been used for many years to drive the timer units see: Timers Chapter.

This dismantled pump shows the component parts of a P.M. pump unit. However only complete units are available as replacement items.

Shown is the induction stator of a ump. The shaded poles are clearly visible by the two bands of copper inserted in opposing poles. Note the orientation of the copper bands before removing the stator from the pump. If the stator is refitted back to front, the pump will run in the opposite direction and not pump at all.

counter clockwise, a small plastic cam is positioned within the casing (seen as a small plastic pip on the rear of the motor casing), which allows rotation in

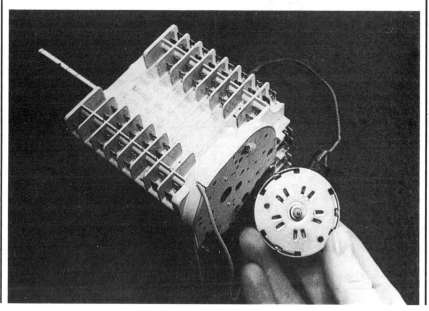

one direction only. Should the motor try to start in the wrong direction, it hits the plastic cam which flicks it back, thus inducing correct rotation.

The ability to run in both directions is utilised to its full extent when this style of motor is used to drive an outlet pump impeller. Should the impeller of the pump come into contact with an item such as a button (this would normally jam/stall a normal shaded pole motor) the motor may be nudged into revolving in the opposite direction and clear the blockage or continue to pump whilst running in the opposite direction.

The construction of the p.m. pump helps alleviate the problem of shaft seal leaks and bearing failure which are common to shaded pole versions, see photos.

This Zanussi motor is visibly similar to the Bendix motor, except for the round control block. This can also be found with a centrifugal pulley (as with the Candy, below).

Centrifugal pulleys

The centrifugal or variomatic pulley is the large pulley that can be seen on some induction motors in such as the Candy, Ariston and Zanussi machines.

What does it do?

It is fitted to help increase the drum speed when the machine spins.

This Candy motor has a centrifugal clutch/pulley system that increases the spin speed.

Why have complex pulleys?

The reason for having adjustable pulley drives relates mainly to the need for faster spinning at the end of the wash cycle. As can be seen from the description of how main induction motors work, their direct speed is limited. Adding a large pulley to the motor to create an increase in drive ratio to the drum pulley

Shown is a Fagor motor, typical of the new style induction motors, that are capable of variable speed build up via a module. Note the tacho connector at the rear of the motor.

for the spin, causes problems. The low speed wash action would require extra windings to slow the rotation whilst high spin speeds would be affected by lack of torque as the number of poles are reduced to increase the motor speed. In the past when spin speeds were much slower (500–800 rpm) the induction motor was the ideal choice. However, the need for ever faster spin speeds has out-stripped the capabilities of the normal induction motor. To compesate for this inability to comfortably reach higher drive speeds further mechanical additions have been made to the drive pulley and in some instances (Candy) to both drive and drum pulley. Some Zanussi machines use a gear and clutch arrangement to help in increasing the drive speed of their induction motor, see photo. Both of these systems are still limited to a drive ratio that produces a maximum spin speed of 1000 rpm (of the drum).

Universal brush motors are required for machines with spin speeds that exceed 1000 rpm (many modern machines now attain 1400 rpm).

How does it work?

Weights within the pulley are 'pushed outwards' by centrifugal force when a fast motor speed is selected. As the pulley is constructed in two halves, the outward movement narrows the gap between the front and back plate of the pulley, therefore increasing its diameter.

This increase in diameter increases the drive ratio between the drum pulley and the motor

Ariston motor with centrifugal pulley system. The motor is only supported at the rear by two large rubber mounts. This allows the weight of the motor to automatically tension the belt as the pulley size increases and decreases in relation to the motor speed.

pulley. When the motor speed slows, the reverse occurs, i.e., the back plate moves away from

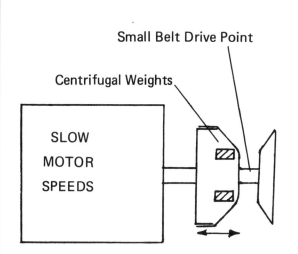

Centrifugal Weights
Small Belt Drive Point

SLOW MOTOR SPEEDS

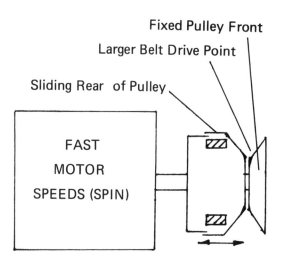

Fixed Pulley Front
Larger Belt Drive Point
Sliding Rear of Pulley

FAST MOTOR SPEEDS (SPIN)

OPERATION OF A CENTRIFUGAL PULLEY SYSTEM

the front plate, and the belt rides on the smaller diameter of the pulley. This can be seen in the photograph of the motor at rest.

Similar clutches can be found on Ariston and Philips machines. Candy machines also have a similar centrifugal pulley on the drum, although this opens at the higher speeds, thus giving a smaller drive ratio. This produces an increase in speed with a constant belt tension, without having to resort to expensive motor windings. **Do not** overtighten the drive belt on machines with a centrifugal pulley. **Note:** Some are self-tensioning by the weight of the motor, i.e., motor only supported by rubber mounts on the rear end frame, allowing weight of the motor to tension the belt and the motor to rise as the pulley size and drive increases during the spin.

The addition of a mechanical pulley system to an otherwise simple and reliable motor increases the risk of faults. In addition to the normal induction motor faults, problems occur with the mechanical action of both centrifugal motor pulleys and drum pulleys (if fitted). Due to the belt being constantly squeezed along its edges, belt wear is accelerated and regular checks are advised. Renew if suspect as spin efficiency will decrease and/or excessive noise will occur.

Pulleys are made either of plastic or cast aluminium and as such, wear ridges form on the belt contact faces. This may lead to restricted movement of the belt resulting in poor drive (poor wash, spin or both), noise, excessive belt wear or jamming and finally, possible motor failure.

The Zanussi geared systems are similar, with noise and internal gear wear being the most common problems. There are no individual spare parts available for these types of drive pulleys, therefore if faults do occur, complete pulleys will be required. However, it is not uncommon from some manufacturers to supply the pulley and motor as one unit, no matter what the fault.

This Zanussi induction motor has a large metal drive pulley with internal gearing and a centrifugal clutch system.

Chapter 27

Suppressors

What is a suppressor?

A suppressor is a device designed to eliminate the formation and transformation of spurious radio waves that may be produced by the operation of the motor and switches within the appliance during normal operation. When switching occurs within the appliance and it is not suppressed, small sparks at the contact points or brushes may produce interference on radio and TV channels or audio equipment plugged into the same electrical circuit, i.e., not only through air waves, but also down the mains cable.

Why should all appliances have them?

By law, all domestic appliances must be suppressed to conform to the regulations on radio interference, and it is an offence to use an appliance that is not suppressed to these standards.

Where are they located?

Suppressors vary in style, shape, position, size and colour. Sometimes individual parts are suppressed, but more often the mains supply is suppressed at or just after the entry point into the appliance. This is called 'in-line' suppression as both the live and neutral supply goes through the suppressor and on to supply the whole of the appliance with power. Do not confuse the suppressors with capacitors which may be used in the appliance for induction motor starting. They may look very similar, but carry out distinctly different functions. Suppressors may also be called 'mains filters' because of their ability to remove spurious radio transmissions.

A revised version of

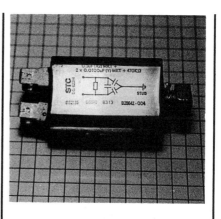

Later style square type suppressor unit.

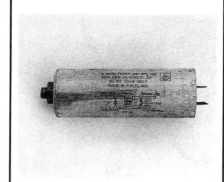

Old style in line suppressor (variations possible).

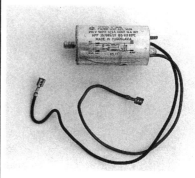

New style in line suppressor (variations possible).

suppression unit can be found in addition to those described above. This is an induction coil, fitted in series between the neutral position at the terminal block and the shell of the machine. As an induction coil is of a far heavier gauge, it only passes suppression current, whereas the two earlier versions carry the full voltage load. Some machines have a combination of both in-line and induction coil types of suppressor. All versions require a good earth path on both plug and socket, see *Basics — Electrical*.

Faults with suppressors (filters)

The main fault is one of short circuit to earth usually resulting in the unit 'blowing' both the main fuse and itself. This is often accompanied by a pungent burnt smell. Renewal is a straightforward one for one replacement.

Open circuit problems can occur and the unit will fail to allow current to pass through as normal. The suppressor can easily be checked for continuity using a meter, see *Using a meter* chapter. When checking, inspect the top insulation closely and if cracked or at all suspect, renew complete unit.

It is common for in-line suppressors to use the earth path as part of their filtering circuit (although very little power passes through it). It is essential for ALL appliances to have a good earth path. If an appliance with an in-line suppressor/filter has a break in its earth path (due to cable, plug or socket fault) small electric shocks may be experienced when the user touches metal parts of the appliance, especially if they are in touch with a good earth path themselves, e.g., holding metal sink or work top, etc. It is essential that such faults are traced and corrected immediately, see *General Safety Guide and Basics — Electrical* chapters.

Although the continuity of a suppressor (lead through type) can be checked easily, its function of suppression cannot be so easily checked. If all other checks, i.e., good earth connection (check for loose/poor connection to shell of machine) no cracks or loose/heated terminals, etc., prove to be satisfactory, and interference to other equipment persists, renew the suppressor.

An alternative means of suppression may be found, especially on microprocessor controlled machines. This is a choke type and may be fitted in series between live and neutral positions or individually in-line on both live and neutral supplies to individual components. Such units consist of a ferrite core or ring around which the conductor is wound.

Some appliances use a combination of different types of suppressor. Suppressors of any type should not be by-passed or omitted as to have an unsuppressed appliance is an offence owing to the interference that it may cause to others, and in the case of 'chokes', failure or omission of this device may cause damage to or corrupt electronic circuits within the appliance, see *Timers (Programme Control)*.

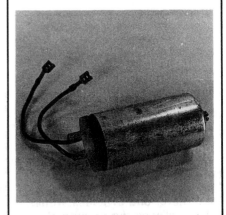

Blown suppression unit.

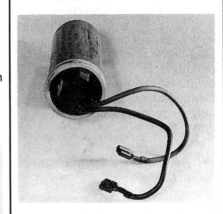

Not all faults are as obvious as the blown unit shown. Check the part thoroughly, this suppressor has a crack in the top insulation and internally a direct short circuit to earth (its metal case). As a result it blew the appliance's fuse when plugged in.

Typical 'choke' suppressors.

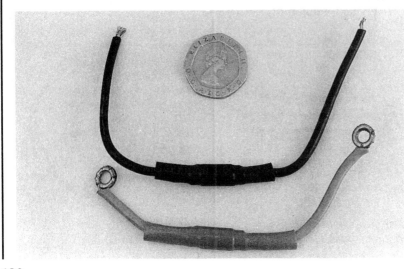

Chapter 28

Bearings

This chapter deals predominently with the main drum support bearings, although many of the associated problems also relate to other areas such as main motor bearings and pump motors (on machines which use ball race or roller bearings in these items). For items which contain sleeve bearings, see *Pumps* and *Motors* chapters.

Types of bearing

Basically, there are three types of bearing used in washing machines.
1. The sleeve bearing. This is simply a phosphor bronze bush in which the motor shaft is free to rotate. It is most commonly used in shaded pole pump motors and reference to that section will give further detail.
2. Ball race bearing. This type of bearing consists of an outer ring in which a small inner ring is supported by circular ball bearings and is free to rotate.
3. Taper roller bearing. The taper roller bearing uses rollers in place of the ball bearing in (2) and as its name implies, the design angles the rollers to give a tapered appearance. The outer ring (shell) is not fixed as with

Shown are both unshielded and shielded ballrace bearings.

the ball race type, and is fitted into position separately. It is essential that taper bearings are fitted as a matched pair, i.e., inner and outer. If this is not done, then the result will be early failure.

The type of bearings used on the main drum bearing assembly will differ not only between manufacturers, but also between models from one manufacturer, i.e., one range may use ball race bearings when a similar model from the same

manufacturer will have taper roller bearings. Although there are only two types of bearing used, the variations in size of both outer and inner are vast, so therefore it is essential to fit identical bearings when replacing old or damaged ones and ensure that all shaft seals and spacers are renewed at the same time. If possible, obtain a bearing kit to make sure that all relevant parts are renewed. Do not cut corners by replacing only one bearing in a set of two or fitting a new taper roller inner to an existing outer shell because the old outer shell is difficult to remove. These short cuts will lead to premature failure and further damage. Be warned!

Why do bearings fail?

There are several reasons why bearings fail, apart from the normal wear and tear over a long period of time. What follows is a list of the most common causes and points to watch out for:

A. The most common failure of both ball and taper bearings is the ingression of water and detergent into the bearing housing. This is usually due to wear or premature failure of the shaft seal. Two types of seal are used. The first one is a simple shaft seal which is pressed into the bearing housing on top of the front bearing. When assembled, the lower section of the drum shaft locates within the seal, usually a raised metal shoulder or collar of mild steel or more commonly phosphor bronze, and is fixed to the base of the drum shaft.

The seal has either one or two spring-loaded lips which press firmly around the collar to create a watertight seal. Normal wear, fluff or scale may break this seal down and allow water and detergent into the bearings quickly resulting in failure. Ensure that the collar is secure on the shaft and clean and that both seal and bearings are renewed at the same time. The second type of seal is a carbon face seal. This system relies on two smooth faces of carbon (or ceramic) that are pressed firmly together when assembled. One face is free to rotate, being fixed to the base of the drum shaft, whereas the other, as before, is fixed on top of the front bearing and is spring-loaded. The two smooth surfaces held under the pressure of the spring within the seal creates the movable watertight seal. Again, fluff, scale and normal wear will lead to water ingression.

Ensure that the fixed carbon ring is smooth, not cracked and securely fixed to the base of the shaft. Check the new spring loaded face seal in a similar way

The carbon face ring at the bottom of this drum shaft is cracked and was the cause of the failure of the bearings, if not spotted it would have led quickly to damage and failure of the new bearings.

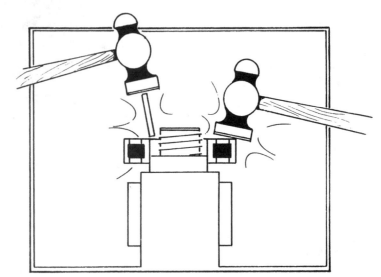

DO NOT hammer directly on the bearing.

and make sure that it seats correctly into the bearing housing. Application of a little sealant is recommended to make certain of a watertight fit to the housing. Do not allow any sealant or dirt on either of the faces of the seals when assembling them.

B. Bearings will also fail if incorrectly fitted. Do not hammer in the bearing (or shell, if taper roller type) directly with a hammer as this may crack or chip it. Do not force the bearing or shell into distorted or dirty housings as this will distort the bearing and create overheating resulting in failure. Inspect the drum shaft closely for ridges or rust which again will distort the inner race of the bearing resulting in overheating or if worn, create a loose fit. Take care to clean all areas and fit only the correct size of bearings carefully.

C. Inspect failed bearings closely for they will have sizes stamped

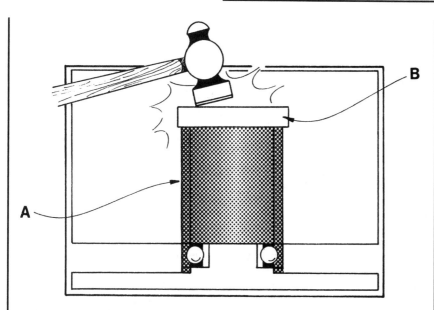

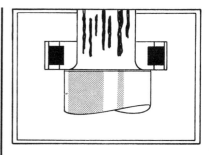

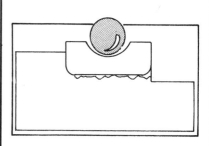

If bearings cannot be pressed into position, use a metal tube (A) of similar diameter and a metal plate (B) to insert the bearing evenly.

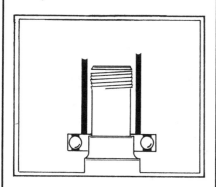

When fitting a bearing only apply force to the non moving part of the bearing.

on them which can be used to ensure the new bearing is of the same dimensions. Failed bearings may also give an indication as to why they failed. Rust would indicate that the seal had failed and prompt closer inspection, cleaning or renewal of the shaft, collar or carbon face. Bearings that are dark blue in colour are usually the result of overheating. Check shape of housing and shaft and do not over-grease. Flakes of metal from the bearing also indicate some form of

distortion or ingress of dirt during assembly.

D. Do not overtighten bearings (especially taper roller types) hoping that it will help seating. The result is usually overheating and premature failure.

Recognising bearing failure

Noise can be a good guide to early recognition of bearing problems. Simply removing the drivebelt should help ascertain if the faulty bearing is in the motor or the drum shaft support bearings. A selection of noise faults are given below along with possible causes.

The above drawings illustrate the problems that occur if a bearing is fitted to a scoured shaft.

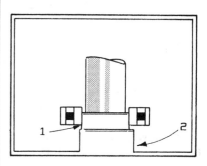

Ensure the new bearing fits up to its locating point and does not leave a gap as shown in (1). Always ensure that the collar (2) is secure and clean.

Noises	Possible cause
Loud rumbling especially on spin.	Collapsed front drum bearing or seized front bearing. This often results in shaft damage if not attended to quickly.
Rattling with intermittent knocking.	Ball or roller of bearing defective.
Rattling/knocking proportional to speed.	Inner or outer of bearing faulty.

High pitched metallic noise.

Common on worn motor bearings at high speed and on new bearing if it has been forced on to a damaged or over-sized shaft.

High pitched ringing noise.

Indication that bearing has been fitted to a damaged housing or fitted carelessly.

Grating and crunching noise.

Collapsed bearing cage or dirt between inner and outer race.

Squeaking.

On old bearing, usually due to lack of lubrication or ingress of water past shaft seal.

May also occur when new bearings are fitted to machine with carbon face type seals if care was not taken to keep both surfaces clean or if check was not carried out for cracks or scouring on carbon faces.

Tips on fitting

To gain maximum life from any bearing, care must be exercised when handling and fitting it. Prior to stripdown and removal of the old bearings, ensure that a note/drawing is made of the position of seals, clips and washers, etc. Inspect both the shaft and housing closely for defects. Ensure the shaft, housing, work area and hands are clean. Remove the new bearing from its protective packaging only when you are ready to fit it.

Ideally, bearings should be pressed into position, but in reality however, this is not always possible and some means of drifting the bearing into place will be required. Great care must be taken if this method is used as damage can easily be done to the bearing at this stage. Endeavour to use a tube when fitting the bearing to enable an equal force to be applied. The tight fitting part of the bearing should take the force only, i.e., if fitting to a shaft, contact should only be with the inner race and when fitting a bearing into a housing, only the outer race should take the force. Do not apply any force to the part of the bearing that is free to rotate during fitting. To assist in fitting bearings, expansion and contraction with heat can be used, although excessive heat must be avoided.

Fitting a bearing or taper roller bearing outer shell into its housing can be assisted by simply putting the bearing or shell into the household freezer for a while and warming the housing with the aid of a light bulb for a hour. This simple technique can help enormously. When fitting a bearing to a shaft, a reversal is required – cool the shaft and warm the bearing, but be careful not to overheat the bearing (especially sealed bearings) as this may create problems. Do not exceed 100°C.

Many ball-type bearings are greased during manufacture and sealed on both sides. Such bearings do not require any extra lubrication prior to assembly. Roller bearings (and some open cage ball bearings) do require packing with grease. This should be done sparingly as over greasing results in churning of the grease and heating takes place which results in loss of lubrication. Pack the bearing with grease and rotate both inner and outer with the fingers to allow any excess to be pushed out from the moving parts.

Typical tapered bearing change

The following sequence of pictures shows the renewal of a set of drum bearings. In this machine, it was found that the main drum support bearings were worn and water damaged. This was caused by the carbon seal failing and allowing water and detergent to enter the bearing and housing.

This was suspected because of the noise of the machine, especially on spin and confirmed by removing the drive belt from the motor to the drum pulley, spinning the drum slightly by hand and listening for any grating noise. If this had been quiet, the motor would have been spun in the same way to test its bearings.

To confirm the drum bearing fault, another simpler method is to open the door of the machine and move the bottom of the door seal so as to see the inner drum and outer tub gap clearly, then try to lift the top lip of the drum only. At this point, the gap between the outer tub and inner drum should not increase nor decrease in size and no movement should be felt other than that of the outer tub on its suspension. This applies to all machines irrespective of bearing types. Picture 14 shows that the drum and spider mount was breaking loose from its position on the drum, due to a form of metal fatigue fracturing the drum. The only possible cure for the fracture, was the fitting of a complete new drum assembly. The initial fault was also rectified, being a renewal of the bearings. (The user was unfortunate in needing the drum unit, especially when the support shaft itself was in such good condition).

The removal of the drum and back half assembly on this style of machine is quite straightforward, and this style of drum and back half are fitted to many of the leading makes (including Hoover, Hotpoint, Creda and late Servis) although in each case the size of bearing and type of carbon seal differ slightly between machines. As the bearing kits are complete matched sets, no problems should arise.

After isolating the machine and laying it face down on a suitable surface, the removal of the back panel will reveal the back half and outer securing nuts. All of the nuts and bolts securing the back half and tub should be removed. (If necessary the top of the machine may be removed to gain access to the top bolts.)

When this is done, mark all of the connections to the heater and thermostat and disconnect them. The back half assembly can now be manoeuvred from its position and removed from the back of the machine. (The back half is made watertight by a rubber seal around itself and the tub. If the back half sticks to the tub, and all of the necessary nuts and bolts have been removed, gently prise the back half from the tub ensuring that no excessive force is used.)

The removal of the pulley and bearings can now proceed.

If the bearing set for your machine is of the ordinary ball bearing type, the job is much easier as the old bearing should knock out in one piece. Should this type of bearing 'collapse' or leave its outer shell, the shell can be removed as shown for the taper bearing shell in picture 18. Care must be taken not to go too deep with the drill into the soft aluminium housing.

When greasing the new bearing, (this is obviously not necessary on the sealed bearing type) take care not to over-grease them, as this will not help lubricate it and in fact will considerably reduce the bearing life.

The new taper bearing kit will come complete with an odd shaped aluminium washer that fits between the rear bearing spacer and pulley. This is known as a torque washer and is essential for the correct operation of the bearing. Always fit a new torque washer to this type of bearing if the pulley is removed for any reason. The torque washer is a simple way of putting the taper bearings under a known pressure without the use of a torque wrench.

When fitted together, the torque washer collapses at a given pressure and dispenses with the need for a torque wrench for tightening the pulley bolt.

A full set of instructions for the torque washer will come with the new bearing kit, however I have included a typical bearing change below.

If your machine is of the type with ball bearings, please disregard the paragraph concerning torque washers, as this type of bearing assembly does not require a torque setting. Renewal of this type of bearing is a simple reversal of the strip-down procedure.

1 Bolt
2 Locking washer
3 Washer (small)
4 Pulley
5 'D' washer
6 Spacer (torque washer)
6a Shim (disposable)
7 Washer (thin)
8 Small bearings
9 Bearing sleeve
10 Tub backplate
11 Bearing and sleeve
12 Washer (thick)
13 Carbon face seal

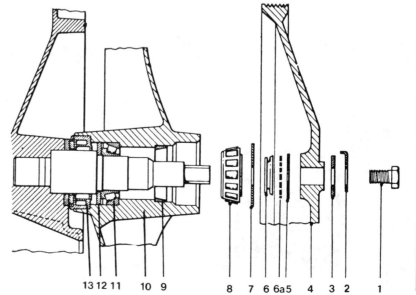

13 12 11   10 9   8 7 6 6a5   4   3 2   1

Instructions for bearing change

1. How to dismantle the old pulley and bearings.

(i) Remove the bolt (1) and washers (2 and 3) securing the tub pulley and remove the pulley (4).

(ii) When removing the tub gasket, check for any wearing. It is advisable to replace this item to ensure a true seal between the inner drum and outer tub.

2. Extraction of old bearings.

(i) The existing bearing sleeves (9 and 11) will be found inside the tub backplate (10). Extract the bearing sub assemblies and then apply heat to the area containing the sleeves. The sleeves can then be gently tapped out with a small chisel, drift or old screwdriver.

3. Renewal of bearings.

(i) Push the new sleeves into place, ensuring that the inner surface of the tub backplate is thoroughly cleaned.

(ii) Insert the first (larger) bearing and washer (12).

(iii) Gently push the seal (13) into place. It is advisable to use a waterproof adhesive around the seal to prevent leaking.

(iv) Clean the new carbon face seal thoroughly to remove all traces of grease, oil, etc.

(vi) It is advisable to fit new washers to the front and rear (12 and 7) as it is likely they have been scoured by the faulty bearings. (Many bearing kits do not contain items 12 and 7 and these may have to be obtained separately.

4. Inserting the torque washer.

(i) Re-assemble the remaining parts in reverse order to that in which they were removed. Do not use the old torque washer (6) – Only use the new washer supplied with the kit.

(ii) Fit the shim washer from the kit under the torque washer. (In the position shown in (6A)).

(iii) Tighten the bolt (1) against the pulley as far as possible without locking the tab washer.

(iv) Complete the tightening operation until the 'D' washer fits firmly against the shoulder of the spider unit. (5).

(v) The spacer is now pre-set. It is essential to do this, in order to ensure the correct loading pressure on the bearings.

5. Discard shim and complete re-assembly.

(i) Remove the bolt (1), washers (2 and 3), pulley (4) and spacer

(6). Discard the shim (6A).

(iii) Re-assemble in reverse order again. This time locking the tab washer against the bolt.

(iv) Failure to follow this procedure on taper roller bearings will result in shortening the life of the new bearing set considerably.

Below are a few helpful hints on the refitting of the assembly back in the machine.

(a) It is advisable to remove the heater from the back half before refitting the back half and drum into the machine. Refitting the heater in this fashion ensures the correct location of the internal heater securing clip.

(b) A thermostat pod (if applicable) and the heater grommet can be helped by a smear of sealant to help slide them into position. If the thermostat grommet looks perished, this should be changed.

(c) Remember to reseal any hoses on the pressure system if they have been disturbed.

(d) Always remember to fit a new tub back half seal.

(e) Check the tension on the main drive belt and adjust the belt if necessary. This is done by moving the motor up or down to slacken or tighten the belt. (Like adjusting a fan belt on a motor car.). Do not overtighten the belt.

Main drum bearing repair (Hoover)

1. Isolate the machine and remove the rear panel. Note all connections to the back plate.

2. Protect the face of the machine and gently lay the machine on its front.

3. Note the position and angle of pressure vessel and remove.

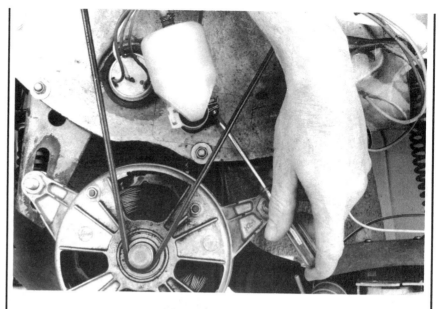

4. Note connections on the thermostat. Remove thermostat with the wires still connected. Use a flat bladed screwdriver to ease it from the seal.

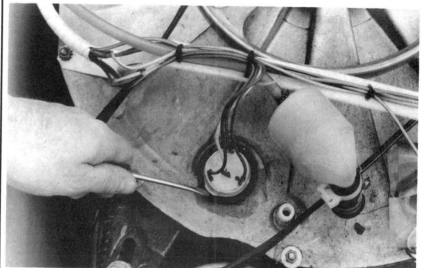

5. Having noted the heater wiring connections, they can now be removed. Slacken the heater clamp nut and gently prise the heater free.

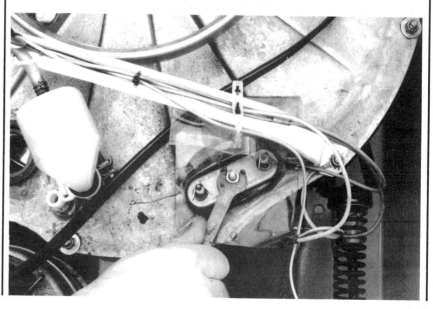

6. Remove back half bolts from around the perimeter of the tub.

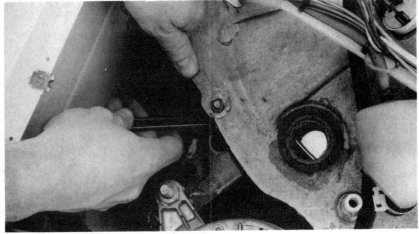

7. The discharge from the drain hole can be seen here, and indicates water penetration of the bearings. The discharge is a mixture of grease, rust and water.

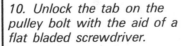

9. With drum and bearing unit completely removed from the machine it is much easier to work on.

10. Unlock the tab on the pulley bolt with the aid of a flat bladed screwdriver.

11. Remove the pulley bolt, pulley and spacers, etc., noting their correct order.

8. With all fixing bolts removed and wires secured out of the way, the drum and back half can be manoeuvred free from the tub.

12. Backplate freed from the drum shaft. (The front bearing may seize on the shaft and will have to be drawn off with pullers. If this happens, protect the shaft end by re-fitting the bolt onto the end of the shaft. This protects the shaft and aids the locations of the puller centre).

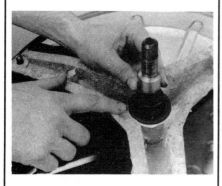

13. Check shaft carefully for wear and ridges at the bearing support points. (Front and rear). Also check carbon face for cracks or loose fit. The example shown is OK.

14. (see photo 12) Check the three mounting points for cracks, etc. This drum and shaft are crush bolt fitted, therefore any fault on the drum or shaft requires a complete drum. Not all machines have this system.

15. Insert screwdriver and prise out bearing carbon face seal.

16. Remove old washer and front bearings. In this case a taper bearing was found. Ball bearings will have to be knocked out with a metal drift.

17. With rear bearing removed, knock out rear bearing shell/liner by the inner lip.

18. If there is no visible lip to the front bearing shell, drill two slots opposing each other in the inner of the housing to expose the liner. Do not drill too deeply.

19. Position of drill mark on front inner bearing sleeve.

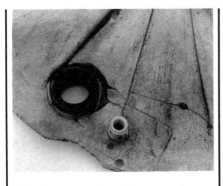

20. Remove the old thermostat seal if it is found to be a poor fit, or perished. Apply sealant to the new seal to ensure a good watertight seal.

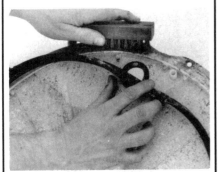

21. Clean all seal and bearing surfaces prior to refitting new parts.

22. New set of taper roller bearings, torque washer and carbon seal suitable for this machine.

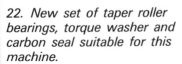

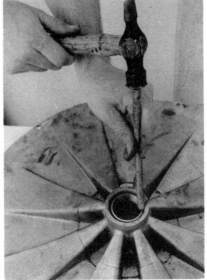

23. Typical set of ball bearings. Seals and bearing sizes may differ. Not interchangeable with taper bearings, not suitable for this machine.

24. Insert rear bearing liner and tap into position firmly, seating to its base using a soft metal drift.

25. Now insert front liner and repeat operation as in step 24.

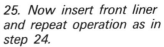

26. Grease bearings back and front and re-assemble as described in text.

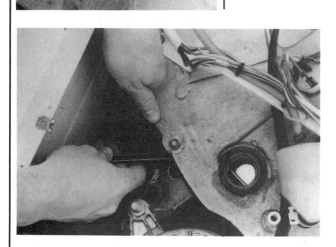

27. Back half ready to be fitted to the drum shaft.

28. Following the instructions for use of torque washer and shim, the unit is made ready for fitting back into the machine. Make sure that you reset the lock tab on the pulley bolt.

29. Tighten the bolts in sequence slowly using opposing bolts. Do not overtighten.

30. Seal and refit all hoses and grommets and secure all connections to the heater, etc. Adjust the belt tension prior to the functional test with all panels in position.

Hotpoint drum bearing removal

1. With machine isolated, open door and remove the securing screws for the plastic surround for the door seal.

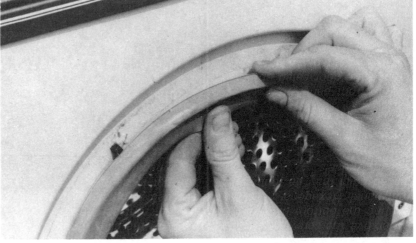

2. Next, remove the door seal surround carefully. This is in two halves (top and bottom).

3. Free the door seal from the outer shell lip of the machine and allow to rest on inside of the front panel.

4. Remove the screws holding the timer knob in position. On early models, only one plastic screw will be found.

5. Pull to remove the soap drawer and remove the exposed screws. This allows the front facia to be removed.

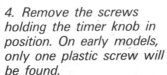

6. Remove the screws securing the top of the front panel.

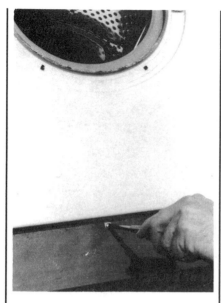

7. Remove the screws securing the bottom of the front panel. Hexagonal headed bolts may be found on early models.

10. With the clips removed, the tub front can be removed completely. Take care not to damage heater or connections.

11. Remove the screws securing the rear panel to expose the drum pulley.

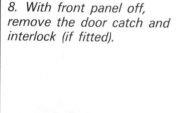

8. With front panel off, remove the door catch and interlock (if fitted).

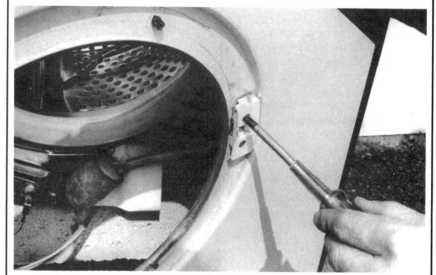

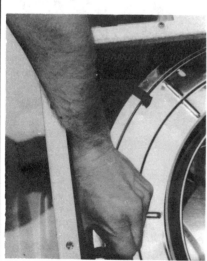

9. Note the position of the clips securing the front of the outer tub and remove carefully.

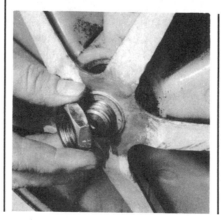

12. Remove the pulley lock nut (right hand thread) and 'chock' the pulley against the tub with a wedge of wood.

13. With the pulley securely wedged, grasp inner paddles of the drum and turn anti-clockwise. This will unscrew the pulley.

14. With pulley removed, tap the drum shaft free from the bearings using a soft-headed mallet.

15. Withdraw the drum and shaft from the tub. This will allow ample room to 'drift' out the ball bearings and shaft seal. Bearing replacement for this type of drum is quite straight-forward, using a soft drift, knock the new bearing home, taking care not to damage the new seal. Re-assembly of your machine is a reversal of the previous procedure.

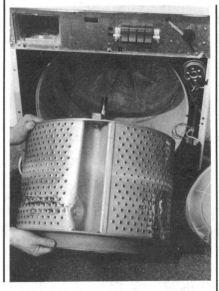 

16. This machine also had severe drum damage as indicated.

17. This style of machine has a 'catch pot' style filter in the sump hose. When removed a large amount of coins, metal screws, curtain hooks and various other household items were found.

18. These items should not have been allowed to enter the machine. They have damaged the drum severely. What would have been a relatively inexpensive 'bearing only' repair, has now required the renewal of a costly drum. (The £1.44 that was found did not cover the cost of the new drum!). This could have been avoided with a little care and attention to pockets, etc., when loading the machine.

Bearing changes needing tub removal

Often the restricted rear access or reverse tub construction will not allow for the renewal of the bearings or drum in the manner previously described. In such instances, for repairs to or renewal of the drum bearings, tub seals or outer or inner drum renewal it may be necessary for the whole of the outer and inner drum unit to be removed from the shell of the machine before further stripdown can take place. There are two main reasons why this course of action may be required.

1. Access to the rear of the outer tub is restricted because of the very small access panel on the rear of the shell of the machine. However, on machines with external cast-iron bearing holders, it is usually possible to manoeuvre the whole bearing unit out through the opening after first laying the machine face down and removing the securing bolts and pulley. Several Zanussi and Ariston models may have bearings fitted in this way but for inner drum removal/renewal, the whole unit would need to be removed as described, see below.

2. The construction of the outer tub is jointed at the front of the machine and not the rear as is usual in most machines, and the inner drum can only be removed by first removing the front of the outer tub. Unfortunately, in most instances the front shell of the machine is not removable and so the whole unit needs to be removed as described.

Most models in the Candy range of machines require tub unit removal for both bearing or drum problems.

It is not uncommon for manufacturers to buy in products from another manufacturer and then 'badge' it as their own. This leads to a mix of model designs throughout the range. Until fairly recently, the current production machines were merely updated variations on basic design, and therefore some continuity and standard format existed.

However, this is not always the case nowadays which means that each machine has to be assessed prior to carrying out repairs, e.g. are the bearings mounted in a detachable housing? If access requires removal of the front of outer tub, can the front of the machine be removed to allow main unit to remain in situ? (see Hotpoint photo sequence).

If no other option exists, the outer tub unit complete with drum and bearing will have to be removed to allow for complete stripdown. The removal of this large unit is via the top of the machine shell. The following text describes the removal of the outer tub unit after removing such items as the top/bottom tub weights, pulley, all connections and hoses and electrical connections to the unit. A photo sequence is not used for this as it would tend to mislead rather than help as each machine will have distinct variations depending on the original manufacturer.

It is advisable to remove all knobs from the front of the machine to reveal the fixing screws of the items behind them when servicing the drum, bearings, outer tub and seals which entails the removal of the outer tub unit from the machine via the top of the machine's cabinet as a complete unit. These should be unscrewed and the components laid over the front facia of the machine. If possible do not disconnect any wiring, but detailed notes of all connections and fixings should be kept in the event of items getting misplaced or dislodged. Release the screws securing the dispenser unit to the cabinet and remove the dispenser hose from the dispenser unit. Lay the dispenser unit over the front of the machine. Remove the top tub weight (if fitted) and release the front fitting of the door seal. To help slide the tub unit out of the machine, two pieces of wood (2" x 1" x 4') can be inserted

down the left-hand side of the machine between the tub and cabinet to support the tub during its removal (see diagram 1). **Note:** If your machine has the timer on the opposite side to that shown in diagram 1, the wood should be inserted down th right-hand side and the machine laid over correspondingly. Now lower the machine onto the left-hand side after making sure that the cabinet side and floor are protected, and release the shock absorber or friction damper mountings. Now disconnect the sum hose, pressure hoses, heater connections, thermostat connections and motor block connections. Remove the drive-belt and drum pulley and check that all connections are free from the outer tub unit. At the top of the machine, release the suspension springs by pushing the tub unit towards the top of the machine. It will now be possible to slide the tub assembly out of the cabinet. At this point a little help may be useful as the unit will be quite heavy and needs manoeuvring out of position. At this time ensure that the lower friction plate is being supported by one of the wooden strips. Hold the door open during the tub withdrawal. Once removed, the unit is then easily accessible and the bearing renewal is similar to that shown in the previous photo sequence. Make a note of all clamp positions, tub front and back positions, etc. It is advisable to re-seal and check all hoses and their fixing points prior to refitting the unit. It is important to do this when the tub is out of the machine as this may be difficult when the unit is replaced. Refitting is a reversal of the removal procedure. After refitting, ensure that all electrical and earth connections are replacing correctly and securely and an R.C.D. protected socket is used when the functional test sequence is carried out. **Note:** Many manufacturers now

have machines on the market with detachable front panels; Philips, Fagor and Hotpoint are three of these. The latter being the version with the plastic/nylon outer tub fitted. See Hotpoint photo sequence. With this type of machine, the drum and bearing assemblies can be removed and changed with the outer rub in situ, thus avoiding the extra work involved in tub removal. Plastic/nylon outer tubs are not used on combined washer dryer machines. With the Hotpoint machine, the pulley is threaded to the shaft and is secured by a locknut. To release the pulley, chock it with wood and rotate the drum anti-clockwise from the front of the machine. When refitting, apply some locking compound to the shaft thread (this can be obtained from any good D.I.Y. or motorists shop).

This picture shows a Fagor machine with the front panel removed, illustrating the excellent access that can be found with this type of machine.

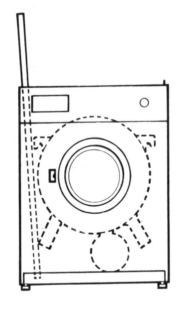

Diagram 1.

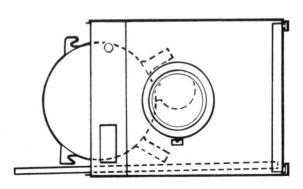

Diagram 2.

Chapter 29

Main drive belts

The drive belts used in automatic washing machines are of two distinctly different types. Both kinds come in a multitude of size variations, but each machine must be correctly fitted with the exact size and type and no other. The two types of belt are — the Vee, so called because of its location on 'V' shaped pulleys, and Multi V belts which are much flatter and have a series of V formations on the drive face. The use of a multi V formation gives a greater contact surface area in relation to the belt width. This is necessary as the belt is designed to be driven by a much smaller and therefore faster rotating drive pulley than the larger single V drive pulleys.

In general Vee belts are to be found on washing machines with induction motors and Multi V belts are found on washing machines with brush gear motors of all types.

What are Vee belts made of?

Both types of belt consist of woven nylon cords upon which a synthetic rubber is moulded. The single Vee belt has sides of approximately 40 degrees and

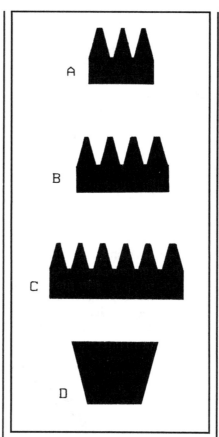

Shown are cross sections of the various types of belt to be found (A) 3 point multi-V. (B) 4 point multi-V and (C) 6 point multi-V. A typical Vee belt cross section is shown in (D).

terminating in a flat base, see cross section D. The Multi V belt is a series of peaks and troughs, the number of which varies with the work load requirements of the belt, see cross sections A, B & C. Always ensure that a replacement belt is the correct size and width, most belts have sizes or size codes printed on the outer face. However, such marks are often illegible on old belts due to wear. Take a note of the make, model and serial number of your machine along with any legible belt code when obtaining a new belt.

Removal and renewal

The single V belt drive system requires both drive pulley (the one on the motor) and drum. pulley (the larger one on the drum shaft), to have a recessed groove the same dimensions as the belt. Multi V systems can have two variations.
1. Both drive pulley and drum pulley are grooved to accept the Multi V configuration of the belt.
2. Only the drive pulley is grooved (to aid grip on its much smaller surface area) and the drum pulley is smooth and slightly convex in shape. Grip is

created on the drum pulley purely by it having a greater contact area to the belt when in use even though this is only on the peaks of the belt. The convex shape keeps the belt in place on the grooveless pulley and reduces wear if misalignment occurs.

Belt care

Ensure pulleys are in good condition, i.e. not chipped or buckled, etc., and are aligned correctly. Misalignment will shorten the working life of both types of belt. Poorly aligned belts will shed the rubber compound coating from the nylon cords leaving tell-tale dust or flakes in the base and surrounding area of the machine. This may block the V section of Multi V belts and cause the belt to fly off usually on a spin cycle. Single Vee belts may twist within the Vee section when misaligned. Close inspection of belts is essential and reversing the belt and bending it is the best way to inspect them. Check the full length in this way. If any defects are found, renew the belt.

When removing a belt for inspection or during repair, care must be exercised to avoid damage to the belt itself. Do not use screwdrivers or similar to prise belts on or off as this can easily damage the belt cords and moulding of the soft aluminium pulleys used on washing machines.

Slacken off the motor bolt to reduce tension and pull the belt towards you mid-way between the pulleys whilst carefully rotating the drum pulley slowly clockwise. This will allow the belt to smoothly ride out of position. Reverse this process for refitting. **Note:** It is advisable to use protective gloves as the pulleys on machines can have very sharp edges.

Belt tension

It is natural for some degree of stretching and wear to occur during use which will result in the need for re-tensioning. Some machines may be self-tensioning, i.e., the weight of the motor keeps the belt under tension (this system was popular with some

Adjust belt tension by moving the motor position up or down to attain correct belt displacement.

early washer dryers). However, the majority of washing machines rely on motor adjustment, i.e., two fixed bolts and one slotted, to tension the belt.

Setting the correct tension is essential. Too tight will quickly wear the belt and worse still, it will damage the drive pulley and cause premature motor bearing failure. Too slack and belt slip will occur resulting in poor wash, excessive vibration or heating of the belt which will result in belt damage or failure. On machines with aluminium pulleys, slipping can create ridges on the pulley grooves. If this does happen, the

To inspect a belt turn it inside out and check the whole length thoroughly. The Vee belt shown has clear signs of cracking on its inner surface and shedding of the outer cover material. Renewal is the only answer to such problems.

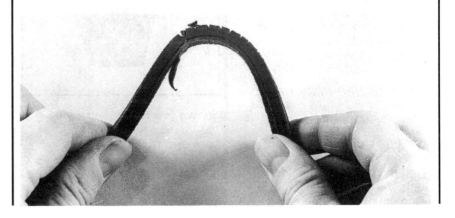

damaged pulley/pulleys will need renewing as any new belt fitted to such a pulley will soon become damaged by the uneven pulley surface.

The correct tension of a belt depends on its free distance between pulley contact points. As a rule a 12mm deflection per 30cm of free belt is required. Most washing machines have in the region of 30cm of free belt between pulleys and therefore a 12 to 13mm deflection is optimum. When fitted and tensioned correctly the belt will have a springy feel. Some stretching will occur to new belts, but modern good quality belts are much less affected. However, the belt will need to be checked at a later date and re-adjusted if required. Do not over-tension a new belt in the misguided hope that this will overcome any initial stretching that may occur.

Points to note

It is not uncommon for belts to be warm after use even when correctly tensioned. This is due to the energy absorbed as the belt flexes and is proportional to the load. If the belt is hot or very warm after use, this would indicate incorrect tension or overloading causing belt slip and friction heating. Correct the problem but check the belt for any cracking caused by overheating. If in doubt, renew the belt.

Noise

This is usually a squealing type of noise most often heard on wash rotation and prior to spin (distribute) when the belt is under most load. This may simply be incorrect tension, i.e., slack, or worn pulleys, i.e., ridges, misaligned or machine overloaded. Again, isolate and correct fault and inspect belt closely for damage. If in doubt, renew it.

Ensure Multi V belts align correctly if both drive and drum pulley are grooved, note position of original belt i.e., first groove on drive pulley is used then first groove on drum pulley is used. Misalignment on Multi V belts is easily done, so ensure that they are correctly fitted to avoid premature belt wear or the belt flying off during spin or wash cycles.

Machines with centrifugal clutch systems, see *Motors* chapter, create quicker belt wear due to the constant squeezing and movement of the belt. Check the drive pulley closely for wear ridges and be prepared to change belts more frequently on this type of drive system to maintain peak performance.

Chapter 30

Using a Meter

Throughout this book, references have been made to meters and their use in continuity testing of individual parts of appliances and their connecting wires. All such testing and checking for 'open' circuit (i.e., not allowing for current flow), must be carried out using a battery powered multi-meter or test meter. **Under no circumstances should testing be carried out on 'live' items**, i.e., appliances connected to the mains supply. Remember to completely isolate the appliance from the mains supply before starting any repair work or testing.

Although some meters or testers have the facility to check mains voltages, I do not agree with their use in repairs to domestic appliances. Faults can be easily traced by simple low voltage (battery power) continuity testing, proving that the simplest of meters or even a home-made one, like the one described, are perfectly adequate for some faults. Remember that safety is paramount and under no circumstances should it be compromised. Always double check that the appliance is unplugged – a good tip is to keep the plug in view so that no-one else can inadvetently plug it

1. *The testing of the heater element to check for a circuit 'through' it. In this instance, the heater does have a circuit as shown by the meter needle. This means that the 'no heat' fault on the machine is not a fault of this component. The next step would be to test the wiring and connections to and from the heater in the same way. Also check the timer and/or the thermostat if in the heater circuit.*

in. The simple home-made continuity tester described later will help trace faults in the wiring of the appliance only. A multimeter like the ones shown will be required for any component testing.

If you decide to buy a test meter, you could find yourself faced with quite a variety to choose from. Do not be tempted to get an over complicated one as it could end up confusing and misleading you when in use. Before using your new meter, read the manufacturer's instructions thoroughly and make sure that you fully understand them. One of the meters used in the photographs is very simple to use when continuity testing and has a scale that reads 'open' circuit or 'closed' circuit. It was purchased from a local DIY store and was very reasonably priced. The meter will also help locate faults with car electrics, but as previously stated, using on live mains circuits should not be entertained.

Some multi-meters are able to show the resistance value of the item being tested as well as indicating continuity. This can be extremely useful if the correct value of the item being tested is known, i.e., correct resistance of

2. The testing of this water valve proved that the coil was open circuit. This is shown by the meter needle staying at its 'rest' position. This shows that the 'no fill' fault on the machine was in fact due to the water valve failing to energise and allow water into the machine. (On components such as these, it is a good idea to try to move the terminals as a poor internal connection may cause an incorrect reading). This problem was cured by renewing the valve.

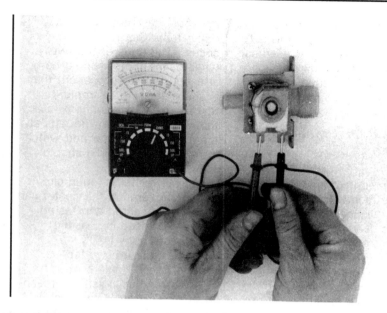

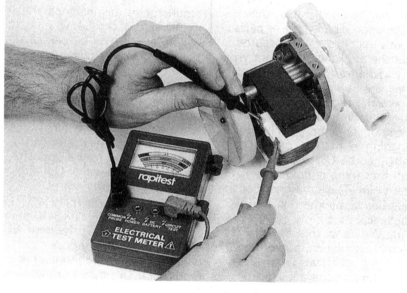

The test on this pump stator proved to be OK, (i.e., closed circuit continuity). This meant that the supply or neutral to and from the pump required checking to discover the reason why the pump failed to work at any point in the programme.

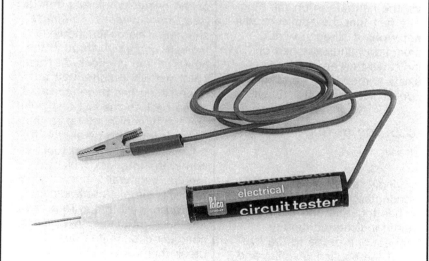

This simple continuity tester was purchased from a local automart for only £2. It is a manufactured version of the home-made type described.

motor winding, armature and element, etc., although this is by no means essential. Detailed use of the multi-meter for this function will be found in its accompanying instruction leaflet.

Electrical fault finding (using a meter)

This simple device can be used to trace wiring faults in most appliances and is very easy to make. It uses the lack of continuity to its full advantage. To make this tester, you will need a standard battery, bulb and three wires (1 x 5" and 2 x 10"). Connect the short wire to the positive terminal of the battery and the other end of that wire to the centre terminal of a small torch bulb. Attach one of the longer wires to the negative terminal of the battery and leave the other end free. The other wire should be attached to the body of the bulb and again, leave the end free.

The two loose ends now act as the test wires. Press the two ends of the wire together, and the bulb will light. If not, check that the battery and the bulb and all connections are O.K. When 'open circuit', the light will stay off, and when 'closed circuit', the light will be on. **Note**: Low voltage bulb type testers of 1.5 volts or 3 volts are unsuitable for testing the continuity of components within the machines. A test meter like the ones shown will be required to test high resistance items such as pumps, timer coil, valves, etc. Ensure that the machine is isolated from the main supply before attempting to use a meter.

How to test for continuity using a meter

To test for an open circuit, note and remove the original wiring to the component to be tested. (If this is not done, false readings may be given from other items that may be in circuit.) The ends of the two wires of the meter should be attached to the component that is suspected. For example, to test a heater for continuity, place the metal probes on the tags at the end of the heater and watch the meter. The needle should move.

If the heater is 'open circuit' i.e., no movement, the heater can then be suspected and tested further. If closed circuit, the heater continuity is OK.

Often the most effective way to trace a fault is to use a very simple but logical approach to them. One such approach is called the "leap frog method" and can be used to find the failed/open circuit part or parts. In this instance, let us assume that the appliance does not work at all when functionally tested, therefore you cannot deduce where the problem lies purely from the symptoms. A quick check of the supply socket by plugging in another appliance known to be OK will verify (or not) that there is power up to that point. This confirms that the fault lies somewhere in the appliance, its supply cable or plug. We know that during normal conditions, power flows in through the live pin on the plug, through the appliance (when switched on) and returns via the neutral pin on the plug. The fact that the appliance will not work at all even when plugged in and switched on indicates that an open circuit exists somewhere along this normal live to neutral circuit.

Leap frog testing – using a meter

First, test that the meter is working correctly, i.e., touch test probes together and the meter should indicate continuity. Connect one probe to the live pin of the appliance's plug and the other on the live conductor connecting point in the plug. Continuity should be found which confirms that the pin, fuse and their connections are alright, but faulty if open circuit occurs. If this check proves to be OK, move the probe from the live conductor point in the plug to the live conductor connection in the terminal block within the appliance. Again, continuity should be found, if not, a fault between plug and terminal block is indicated. **Note**: On cable continuity testing, it is best to move the cable along its length during the test to ascertain if an intermittent fault may exist. If this test is alright, proceed to move the probe to the next convenient point along the live conductor, in this instance, the supply side of the ON/OFF switch, which may be part of the main programme switch on some machines (usually the front terminals). Again, continuity is required. An open circuit indicates a fault between terminal block and switch connection. The next step is to move the probe to the opposite terminal of the switch. Operate the switch to verify correct action (i.e., 'on' continuity 'off' open circuit). If OK proceed to the next point along the wire, in this instance the interlock connection. Again continuity is required. If OK, move probe/wire to the terminal on the return side of the heater within the interlock (see *Door Switches – Interlock* chapter). This again should indicate continuity through the heater of the interlock. At this point we will assume that an open circuit has been indicated, so go back to the last test point and verify continuity up to that point. If found to be alright, then a fault has been traced that lies within the interlock which requires renewal.

This simple, methodical approach is all that is required to find such problems. With more complex circuits it is best to break them down into individual sections, i.e., motor, heater, switch, etc., and test continuity of each section from live through the timer and the individual parts and back to neutral. This may involve moving the live wire that would normally remain on the plug live pin to a more convenient supply point within the appliance to avoid misleading continuity reading from other items within the appliance circuit. With practice, faults can be found even in complex wiring in this way. **Note**: The action of switching within the interlock of power back to the timer cannot be verified, but continuity of the wiring can be checked in a similar leap-frog manner. In this instance, owing to the heater being 'open circuit' the interlock would fail to operate and action of power being retruned (switched) to the timer for distribution to other parts could not take place. A fault with the main switching action of the interlock would have been indicated during the functional test (see *Functional Testing* chapter), i.e., when the machine was switched on, the door locked but nothing else would operate other than the door locking. This is due to most (but not all) machines having the interlock as the first item in circuit when switched 'on', therefore incorrect latching of the

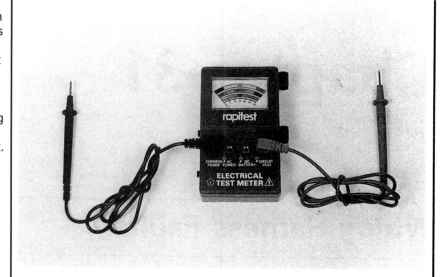

door or failure of the interlock (other than short circuit of the internal switch) will render the appliance inoperable.

DO NOT trace faults by looking for mains voltages. There is no need to consider or use such dangerous techniques. ALL testing can and should only be carried out with the appliance completely isolated (i.e., switch off, plug out) using only a battery powered meter or tester to indicate continuity or open circuit.

The ohms reading will differ from item to item. Test for open or closed circuits only. Any reference to an ohm (Ω) reading

A typical multimeter of the type available in most DIY stores. Try to obtain a meter with a good informative booklet. The meter shown was purchased for under £14.00 and proved to be useful for many other jobs around the house and car.

is a guide only as resistances differ from machine to machine. The objective is to test for either continuity or the lack of continuity of the item being tested.

Chapter 31

Wiring Harness Faults

What is a wiring harness

The term harness is used for all of the wires that connect the various components within the appliance. On large appliances they are usually bound or fastened together in bunches to keep the wiring in the appliance neat and safely anchored. Smaller appliances, however, may sacrifice neatness for safety and route the wiring to avoid contact with heat, sharp edges, etc.

What does it do?

At first sight, the harness may look like a jumble of wires thrown together. This is not the case. If you take the time to inspect the harness, you will find that each wire is colour coded or numbered (either on the wire itself, or on the connector at either end). This allows you to follow the wiring through the appliance easily. With practice, any wiring or coding can be followed.

As most of the wires in the machine either finish or start at the timer unit, it may be helpful to think of the timer as the base of a tree, with the main wiring harness as the trunk. As the trunk is followed, branches appear (wires to the valves, pressure switches, etc.). Continuing upwards, the trunk gets slowly thinner as branching takes place to the motor, pump, module, etc.

Each item is therefore separate but linked to the timer by a central bond of wire. This in turn can be likened to a central command post, communicating with field outposts.

The connecting wires to and/or from a component are vital to that component and possibly others that rely on the correct functioning of that item.

Luckily, wiring faults are not too common, but when they do occur they sometimes appear to result in big problems, when in reality it is only a small fault that has occurred, i.e., one poor connection can cause a motor not to function at all, and render the appliance unusable.

Do not fall into the trap of always suspecting the worst. Many people, including engineers, blindly fit parts such as a motor or a heater for a similar fault to that mentioned, only to find it did not cure the problem. Often the timer is blamed and subsequently changed. This does not cure the problem and is an expensive mistake. Stop, think and check all wires and connections that relate to your particular fault. Always inspect all connections and ensure that the wire and connector has a tight fit. Loose or poor connections can overheat and cause a lot of trouble, especially on items such as the heater.

Poor connections to items such as the main motor or pump will be aggravated by movement of the machine when in use and may not be so apparent when a static test is carried out.

One of the most easily missed faults is where the metal core (conductor) of the wire has broken and the outer insulation has not. This wire will appear perfect from the outside but will pass no electrical current. To test for this, see the chapter: *Using a meter.*

It must be remembered that such faults may be intermittent. That is to say that one reading may be correct and the same test later may prove incorrect. This is due to the movement of the outer insulation of the wire first making, then breaking the electrical connection.

When testing for such intermittent faults, pull or stretch each wire tested. An unbroken wire will not stretch whereas a wire that is broken internally will stretch at the break point and rectification is a simple matter of renewing the connection with a suitable connector. Do not make the connection by twisting the wires together and covering them with insulation tape – use only the correct rating of connector and ensure a secure and insulated joint. If a joint is required in a position of cable movement, e.g., wiring from shell to tub unit components, it is advisable to renew the whole length of wiring or the joint made in a fixed section of cable. The use of rigid connections in movable wiring must be avoided. Take time to do a few simple checks – it saves time, patience and money. **Note**: Ensure that the harness is secured adequately to the shell of the machine, at the same time allowing for free movement of wiring to the motor, heater, etc.

Take care that any metal fastening clips do not chafe the plastic insulation around the wires. Also make sure that wires are not in contact with sharp metal edges such as self tapping screws, etc.

Warning: Before attempting to remove or repair the wiring harness or any other component in the appliance, isolate the appliance from the main electrical supply by removing the plug from the wall socket.

Various harness connections

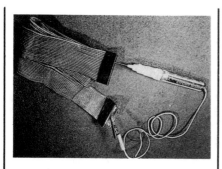

Female spade terminal.

The terminal block is the first distribution point of the power into the machine. Ensure all connections are sound, as heat will be generated if not.

When testing for continuity of the ribbon cable only, insert a metal plate in one end to make contact with all connections as shown. Use a low voltage continuity tester to confirm continuity of each wire. ensure the cable is moved during the test so as not to miss an intermittent fault.

Piggy back terminal for two wires to one terminal.

Harness connector block. Again any loose connectors will overheat and cause problems. Ensure a secure fit.

Male Terminal   Female Terminal

Harness connection. Can often be of a multi block fitting of several wires in one moulded block.

In line connector used for low amperage.

Insulation cover.

Butt connector for connecting several wires together.

Large in line connector used for high amperage wires.

All of the above are 'crimp' fitted to inner and outer of the wires. When used make sure that they fit securely and will not easily part.

Chapter 32

Useful Tips and Information

1. Shown below are the various types of clips in common use in today's machines. In the centre are the screw type wire clips. Top right is the new type toothed clip. This new clip is much easier and quicker to fit as grips or pliers are used to tighten jaws together. Left are two types of corbin spring clips. Care should be taken in removing this type of clip, as they have a tendency to 'spring' — under tension. For removal, corbin pliers are best, however, with care, ordinary grips may be used. Lower right is a worm drive or jubilee clip. This again is a simple but effective clip.

2. Check all hoses thoroughly for perishing and/or cracking. With corrugated hoses (as shown), stretch the hose to ensure a thorough check. (It is wise to check any new hose before fitting).

3. On some machines the door interlock jams the door shut when it fails. As the fixing screws are behind the locked door, it may be difficult to open the door. It may be possible to move the door latch with a screwdriver, as shown. Be careful not to scratch the paintwork.

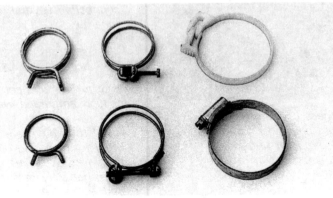

4. A little washing-up liquid or fabric conditioner can be smeared on grommets or rubber mouldings to assist fitting.

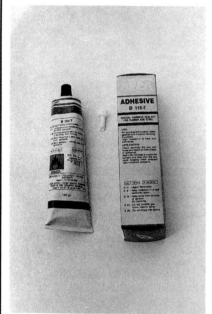

5. Sealants like the one shown can be used for pressure system hoses and for aiding the fitting and sealing of new hoses, grommets, etc.

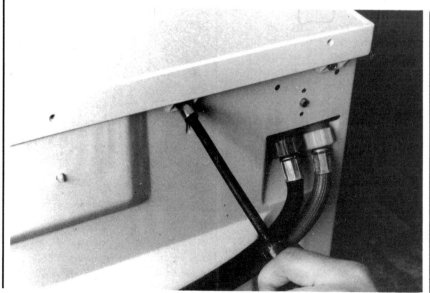

6. Some machines may have a wire surrounding the door seal. This retaining ring can be removed using a flat bladed screwdriver. The machine shown is a Fagor, but many makes use similar fixings.

7. On some machines with fitted worktops, the top removal may not be straightforward. Firstly, remove the self-tapping bolts on the rear plastic panel section.

8. Remove the rear plastic surround completely. As always, ensure that the machine is isolated. This is because many machines will reveal open terminals behind the plastic moulding.

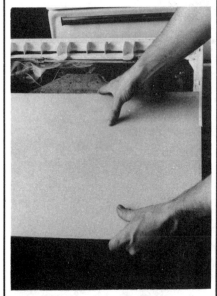

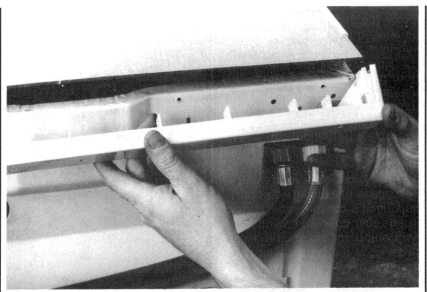

9. The top is now ready to be moved from its position. Push or pull the top towards the back of the machine and remove. This may require some force, especially if the top has not been removed for some time.

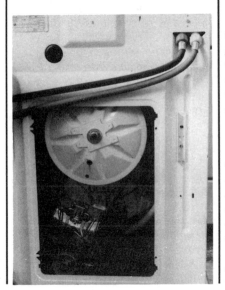

10. Access to the top half of the machine is now possible. To aid the refitting of the top, a little washing-up liquid may be smeared on the plastic slides of the machine.

11. Rear access to this type of machine is limited to a much smaller rear opening. Any repairs to this type of machine will require the inner and outer tub assembly to be removed via the top of the machine. please refer to the chapter on BEARINGS.

Damage or scratches on white appliances can be corrected by using products such as these which are widely available.

Chapter 33

Buying Spare Parts

The aim of this manual has been to assist in the D.I.Y. repair to your automatic washing machine. I hope that now, you will not only have a greater knowledge of how these machines work, but also the knowledge to prevent faults.

Above all, I hope that, armed with this information, you will feel confident enough to tackle most (if not all) of the faults that may arise with your machine from time to time.

However, all this knowledge and new found confidence could be wasted if you are unable to locate the spare parts needed to carry out the repair. In the past this would have been a problem, but in recent years the availability of spares has increased for several reasons:

1. The reluctance of people to pay high call-out and labour charges for jobs that they feel they can do themselves.

2. The general interest in household D.I.Y. coupled with the saving of call-out and labour charges, gives a feeling of satisfaction when the job is successfully completed.

3. The growth in size and number of D.I.Y. stores in recent years.

4. The improvement in the

This small but well stocked shop offers an extremely wide variety of items. Try to locate a similar shop in your own area prior to faults arising. This will save time later on.

availability of pre-packed spares.

Many independent domestic appliance companies have been reluctant to supply parts for the D.I.Y. market in the past, but the current trend is to expand the amount of pre-packed spares.

This has been confirmed by the three biggest independent spares suppliers of genuine and non-genuine (Patterned) spares. The range of 'off the shelf' spare parts in both retail outlets and mail order companies is most welcome, and many machine manufacturers who do not have local dealerships will supply parts by post if requested, (unfortunately this can sometimes be a lengthy process).

One way of obtaining the parts you require is to find a local 'spares and repairs' dealer through the Yellow Pages or local press. This is best done before your machine develops a fault as you will then not waste time when a fault arises. In many instances you may possess more knowledge of your machine than the assistant in the shop, so it is essential to take the MAKE, MODEL and SERIAL NUMBER of your machine with you to help them locate or order the correct spare part for your requirements.

You may also find it quite helpful to take the faulty part(s) with you if possible, to confirm visually that it is the correct replacement. For instance, most pumps will look the same from memory, although quite substantial difference may be seen if the faulty item is compared with the newly offered item. The casing or mounting plate, etc., may be different. It is most annoying to get home only to find that two extra bolts are required.

Patterned parts

Certain parts that are widely available are marked "suitable for" or "to fit". These are generally called 'patterned', or 'patent' parts. Such terms refer to items or parts that are not supplied by the manufacturer of your machine, but are designed to fit it.

Some are copies of genuine parts and others are supplied by the original parts manufacturer to an independent distributor which are then supplied to the retailer and sold to the customer. This avoids the original machine manufacturer's markup as it is not an official or genuine spare part. This saving is then passed onto the customer.

Many of the appliance manufacturers disliked this procedure in the past, as the parts were of an inferior quality, but this is not generally the case today as the supply of parts is very big business and quality has improved dramatically. Although

great savings can be made, care must be taken not to save money by buying inferior spare parts. Check the quality of the item first wherever possible. A reputable dealer should supply only good quality patterned or genuine parts.

Many of the original machine manufacturers are now discounting their genuine authorised spares to combat the growth in patterned spares. This is very good, as it can only benefit you, the consumer.

Genuine parts

Parts supplied by the manufacturer of your machine or by their authorised local agent, are classed as "genuine" and will in many cases, carry the company's trade mark or colours, etc., on the packaging. Many of the parts in today's machines are in fact not produced by the manufacturer of the finished machine, but a sub-contractor who also may supply a distributor of patterned spares with identical items.

Patterned spares producers will only take on items that have volume sales and leave the slow moving items to the original manufacturer of the machine. Generally it is a long procedure to obtain spares 'direct' from the manufacturer as many are unwilling to supply small orders direct to the public. Another system used to deter small orders is to use a 'pro-forma' invoicing sheet that will delay the receipt of parts until your cheque has cleared.

With the increase in D.I.Y., manufacturers are slowly changing their view regarding spares supply. This is simply to fend off the patterned spares, by making the original parts more available and competitively priced. Again this will in turn benefit the consumer.

Parts by post

A free parts list of both patterned and genuine spares for most leading makes of machine can be obtained by writing to:
Dixon R.S.
(Postal spares department)
Cranswick
Driffield
North Humberside
YO25 9QJ
Please enclose a large stamped addressed envelope and the make and model number of the relevant machine(s).

Parts can be obtained by post at competitive prices and payment can be made by cheque, Access or Visa.

Further help and information

A detailed practical and instructional 55 minute video which complements the information given in this publication is also available. For further details please write to the above address.

In conlusion

Finally, the decision between genuine and patterned spares is yours, cost and speed of availablity may have to be taken into consideration, but do not forsake quality for a small financial saving.

As a guide a list of manufacturers' names and contact telephone numbers is given for the U.K. The information shown was correct at the time of publication but changes may occur with the passage of time.

Make	Telephone No.
AEG	0753 872325
Ariston	0322 526933 (or see Yellow Pages under Merloni Domestic Appliances)
Asko (was Asea)	081 568 4666
Bauknecht	0800 555222
Bendix	Yellow Pages
Bosch	081 573 6789
Candy	051 334 2781
Colston	see Ariston (above)
Creda	Yellow Pages
Electra	see Local Electricity Board
Electrolux	0325 300660
Fagor	0707 377877
Frigidaire	051 355 0588
Hotpoint	Local Directory
Hoover	Yellow Pages
Indesit	0322 526933 (Or see Yellow Pages under Merloni Domestic Appliances)
Kelvinator	051 334 2781
Miele	Yellow Pages
Philco	081 902 9626
Philips (now Whirlpool)	0800 101010
Servis	021 526 3199
Whirlpool (was Philips)	0800 101010
Zanussi	Yellow Pages/ Local Directory
Zerowatt	051 334 2781

Chapter 34

Know your machine

Most of us, you'll agree, would be completely lost without the range of gadgets we've become accustomed to using every day. Learning to take advantage of these time and energy-saving appliances, particularly in the kitchen, will give you the freedom to look after yourself and your family in more important ways.

With your special needs in mind, washing machine manufacturers have carefully developed automatic washing machines which will make the task quick and effortless however often you wash. There are several types of washing machines available.

Used properly, a fully automatic washing machine provides a most efficient and thorough method of washing. The special wash action of front and top loaders with a horizontal rotating drum mechanism creates sufficient agitation to effectively remove all dirt particles and even stubborn stains. However, it is important to use the correct type of washing powder in these machines. The low suds washing powder recommended by most major machine manufacturers is Persil Automatic. The free movement given by the controlled lather level lets the clothes be washed thoroughly and efficiently to give perfect results across all machine programmes, from a boil wash to a cool programme for silk and woollens. Automatic machines will also ensure that sufficient rinses are made to remove dirty wash solution leaving your clothes completely clean, fresh and cared for.

Overloading your machine will greatly reduce cleaning efficiency, as free movement of the clothes is restricted. Your machine has a maximum load capacity which should not be exceeded.

On the facing page is a handy table to help you check your dry weight loads compiled with the help of Lever Brothers.

Rule of thumb

To help in assessing the correct wash load, the drawing illustrates the maximum dry load size per selected programme.

A. Woollen and other fine fabrics requiring gentle – only a quarter of the drum should be occupied.

B. Synthetic and man-made fibres requiring delicate washing – only half the drum space should be occupied.

C. Cottons and robust fabrics requiring higher temperatures and normal wash action – can occupy a greater proportion of the drum, leaving approximately a hand's width space at the top.

This information is for guidance only and the spaces represent the space left when the clothes are loaded normally. Do not compress the load to achieve the recommended amount of vacant space.

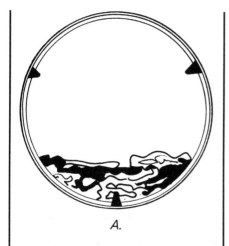

A.

B.

C.

Clothes

Blouse	cotton		150g	(5oz)
	other		100g	(3¹/₂oz)
Dress	cotton		500g	(1lb 2oz)
	other		350g	(12oz)
Dressing Gown			700g	(1lb 8oz)
Jeans			700g	(1lb 8oz)
10 Nappies			1000g	(2lb 3oz)
Nightdress			150g	(5oz)
Pyjamas	cotton		350g	(12oz)
Shirt	cotton		300g	(10oz)
	other		200g	(7oz)
Skirt			200g	(7oz)
Suit, bulked polyester			1500g	(3lb 5oz)
Sweater	wool		400g	(14oz)
	other heavy		350g	(12oz)
	lightweight		200g	(7oz)
Tracksuit			1000g	(2lb 3oz)
Teeshirt			125g	(4¹/₂oz)
Vest			125g	(4¹/₂oz)

Household items

Bedspread	candlewick	(D)	3000g	(6lb 10oz)
		(S)	2000g	(4lb 6oz)
Blanket	wool	(D)	2000g	(4lb 6oz)
		(S)	1500g	(3lb 5oz)
	acrylic	(D)	1500g	(3lb 5oz)
		(S)	1000g	(2lb 3oz)
Cot Sheet			200g	(7oz)
Duvet Cover	cotton	(D)	1500g	(3lb 5oz)
	other	(D)	1000g	(2lb 3oz)
Pillow			900g	(2lb)
Pillowslip			125g	(4¹/₂oz)
Tablecloth	large		700g	(1lb 8oz)
	small		250g	(9oz)
Tea Towels			100g	(3¹/₂oz)
Towel	bath		700g	(1lb 8oz)
	hand		250g	(9oz)
Sheet	cotton	(D)	1000g	(2lb 3oz)
		(S)	750g	(1lb 10oz)
	other	(D)	500g	(1lb 2oz)
		(S)	350g	(12oz)

Chapter 35

Common causes of poor washing results

Poor washing is mainly due to the incorrect operation of the machine by the user, rather than a mechanical or electrical fault of the machine. The most common user faults are listed below.

1. Mis-use of the controls –

(a) To achieve good consistent results from your automatic, you must have a good understanding of your machine and its controls. Always remember – you tell the machine what to do. If in doubt, read the manufacturer's manual.
(b) Does the selected programme have the right water temperature and wash time for the fabrics in the load?

2. Incorrect dosage –

(a) The amount of powder that should use is usually displayed on the side of the powder pack. Please remember that this is only a guide, and the amounts have to be adjusted to load size, type and degree of soiling, and the 'hardness' of the water supply.
(b) Is the container that is used for measuring the powder accurate? On the large sized packs one measure of powder should weigh 3oz. With the recent advent of "compact" powders, use the scoop provided and remember that one scoop is normally equal to 1 cup of the previous bulkier powders.
(c) Have you made allowances for special types of soiling? Ointments, thick creams, heavy perspiration and the like, use up the suds activity very quickly. This can be compensated for by adding an extra half cupful of powder.
   N.B. Poor soil and stain removal, the greying of whites or the appearance of 'greasy balls' on washed clothes is a clear indication of under-dosing. It is never due to over-dosing.

3. Water supply –

   Washing powder is formulated to do several tasks.
(a) Overcome water hardness.
(b) Wet-out the fabrics.
(c) Remove the soiling from the clothes.
(d) Hold the soiling in suspension, away from the clothes.
   It can be seen that the harder the water, the harder the powder has to work. More powder should be added in the case of hard water, less in the case of soft water. The local area water authority should be able to inform you of the hardness of water in your area.

4. Incorrect loading –

(a) Overloading the washer will result in the clothes not being able to move freely inside the drum, resulting in inadequate soil removal.
(b) Some programmes require reduced loads. If one of these programmes is used, reduce the load. If you are not sure, read the manufacturer's manual.

5. Other factors –

(a) How old is the machine? Like any purchase, a washing machine has a restricted lifespan. In the case of an automatic washer, the average lifespan is approximately eight years.
(b) When was the machine last serviced?
(c) Poor whiteness is a result of constant under-dosing (See 4). With the soiling not being removed, there is a gradual build up of deposits in the clothes. This can only be corrected by always washing with the correct loads.
(d) Domestic changes can reflect the quality of the wash, i.e., have

you moved area? (See 3.) Is there a new addition to the family? (See 2c.)

(e) Are the poor results evident on all programmes or only on specific programmes? (See 4.)

(f) Most of the manufacturers recommend an idle wash to keep the machine clean and free from deposits. This means a wash with no powder or clothes, every month or so.

(g) Have you read the manufacturer's manual?

Improvements on poor colours and whites will not happen magically, the process is very gradual. Once a good whiteness has been achieved, correct washing and dosing is the only way to maintain the standard.

6. Do not forget to check pockets for coins and tissues, etc., and fasten all zippers.

Six golden rules for best results

1. Wash clothes frequently. Modern fabrics, particularly the man-made fibres, need frequent washing or dirt may become absorbed into the fibres.
2. Use the right amount of powder.
Refer to the side of the packet of powder for the correct dosage. Under dosing leads to poor soil and stain removal, and the greying of whites.
3. Choose the recommended wash code and machine programme for the fabric. To safeguard colour and finish, preserve shape and minimise creasing, never wash hotter, wash longer or spin longer than indicated by the correct wash code for the fabric.
4. Rinse thoroughly. Thorough rinsing is essential. Some finishes such as shower-proofing lose their effectiveness if not well rinsed; towelling fabrics, particularly nappies, may become harsh and scratchy. Always rinse at least twice.
5. Treat stains quickly.
Give first aid treatment immediately wherever possible by blotting with an absorbent tissue. Never neglect a stain and never rub – this may push it further into the fabric. Pinch out as much as you can.
6. Dry 'easy care' fabrics correctly.
Check the instructions on the label. Easy care fabrics of cotton or man-made fibre, should be rinsed in cold water and should only be put in the spinner for a few seconds.

Chapter 36

Successful stain removal

Stains on washable fabrics fall into two groups:

Group one – stains that will wash out in soap or detergent suds

Type of stain

. Beetroot, Blood, Blackcurrant and other fruit juices, Chocolate, Cream, Cocoa, Coffee, Egg, Gravy, Ice lollies, Jam, Meat juice, Mud, Milk, Nappy stains, Pickles, Soft drinks, Sauces, Soup, Stews, Syrup, Tea, Tomato ketchup, Wines and Spirits and Washable ink.

Method

Fresh stains – Soak in cold suds to keep the stain from becoming set in the fabric. Then wash in the normal way according to the fabric.
Old dried-in stains – Lubricate with glycerine. Apply a mixture of one part glycerine to two parts water to the stain and leave for 10 minutes. Then treat as fresh stains.
Residual marks – White fabrics only. Bleach out with Hydrogen Peroxide solution. (One part 20 volume hydrogen peroxide to nine parts water). Leave soaking in this solution for 1 hour. Then wash in the normal way. Blood stains may leave residual iron mould marks, which should be treated as for iron mould.
Special Note: For 'built' stains such as egg (cooked), chocolate and mud, scrape off surplus staining matter first before putting to soak. Blood and meat juice stains whether fresh or old should be soaked in cold water first.

Group two – 'treat-'n-wash' stains

What you will need

Glycerine (for lubrication)
Methylated Spirit (handle carefully: *Inflammable – Poisonous*).
Turpentine *(Inflammable).*
Armyl Acetate (handle carefully – *Highly inflammable*).
Hydrogen peroxide.
Proprietary grease solvent – 'Thawpit', 'Beaucare', 'Dab-it-off', etc., *(Do not breathe the vapour: Use in a well ventilated room).*
Photographic Hypo.
White vinegar (acetic acid).
Household ammonia (keep away from eyes).
Cotton wool, Paper tissues, etc.

Handy hints

1. Act quickly to remove a stain and prevent it 'setting'. The faster you act, the milder the remedy needed.
2. Never rub a stain, as this pushes it further into the fabric. 'Pinch out' as much as you can, using a clean cloth or a paper tissue.
3. Never neglect a stain. The more drastic remedies for 'set' stains may harm delicate fabrics. If some stains are left on man-made and drip-dry fabrics in particular, they can be absorbed permanently into the fabric itself. Stains such as iron mould (rust) can weaken cellulosic fabrics and may eventually cause holes.
4. When applying solvents, always work from outside the stain towards the centre to avoid making a ring.
5. Always try a solvent on a hidden part first (e.g. under hem or seam allowance) to make sure it does not harm colours or fabric.
6. Stains on garments to be 'dry-cleaned' should be indicated

on the garment (e.g. with a coloured tacking thread). Tell the cleaners what has caused the stain. This facilitates the task of removal and lessens the risk of the stain becoming permanently set by incorrect treatment.

Absorbent pad method

Using two absorbent pads of cotton wool, one soaked with the solvent and other held against the stain. Dab the underside of the stain with solvent and the staining matter will be transferred from the material to the top pad. Change this pad around to a clean part and continue working in this way until no more staining matter comes through. To remove last traces of the stain, wash in usual way.

Type of stain	Solvent	Method
Ballpoint ink	Methylated spirit (INF) (Benzine for acetate and 'Tricel')	Absorbent pad method.
Bicycle oil	Proprietary grease solvent	Absorbent pad method or follow manufacturer's instructions
Black lead	Proprietary grease solvent	Absorbent pad method or follow manufacturer's instructions
Chalks and Crayons (Washable)		Brush off as much as possible while dry. Then brush stained area with suds (one dessertspoonful to a pint of water). Wash in the usual way.
Chalks and Crayons (Indelible)	Methylated spirit. (INF) (Benzine for acetate and 'Tricel'.) (INF)	Absorbent pad method
Chewing gum	Methylated spirit. (INF) (Benzine for acetate and 'Tricel'). (INF)	Absorbent pad method. Alternatively rub the gum with an ice cube to harden it. It may then be picked off by hand. Wash as usual to remove final traces.
Cod Liver Oil, Cooking Fat, Heavy grease stains	Proprietary grease solvent	Absorbent pad method or manufacturer's instructions
Contact adhesives. (e.g. Balsa cement, 'Evostick')	Amyl Acetate. (INF)	Absorbent pad method.
Felt pen inks	Methylated spirit. (INF) (Benzine for acetate and 'Tricel'). (INF)	First, lubricate the stain by rubbing with hard soap, and then wash in the usual way. for obstinate stains, use Methylated Spirit and absorbent pad method. Wash again to remove final traces.
Grass	Methylated spirit. (INF) (Benzine for acetate and 'Tricel'). (INF)	Absorbent pad method.
Greasepaint	Proprietary grease solvent	Absorbent pad method or follow manufacturer's instructions
Hair lacquer	Amyl Acetate, (INF)	Absorbent pad method
Iodine	Photographic Hypo	Dissolve one tablespoon hypo crystals in one pint warm water. Soak the stain for about 5 minutes, watching closely. As soon as the stain disappears, rinse thoroughly, then wash in the usual way.
Iron mould (rust marks)	a) Lemon juice (for wool, man-made fibres and all fine fabrics)	Apply lemon juice to the stain and leave it for 10-15 minutes. Place a damp cloth over the stain and iron. Repeat several times, as necessary. Rinse and wash as usual.
	b) Oxalic acid solution (for white cotton and linen only) use with care	Dissolve 1/2 teaspoonful oxalic acid crystals in 1/2 pint hot water. Tie a piece of cotton tightly round the stained area (to prevent the solution spreading) and immerse the stained part only. Leave for 2 or 3 minutes. Rinse thoroughly and wash in rich suds.

Washing Machine Manual

Type of stain	Solvent	Method
Lipstick and Rouge i) light stains ii) heavy stains	Proprietary grease solvent	Soak then wash in usual way. Absorbent pad method or follow manufacturer's instructions.
Marking ink	Marking ink eradicator (from stationers).	Follow instructions on the bottle label carefully.
Metal polish	Proprietary grease solvent	Absorbent pad method or follow manufacturer's instructions.
Mildew (mould on articles stored damp) a) coloured articles		The only treatment is regular soaking, followed by washing in rich suds – this will gradually reduce the marks.
b) white cottons and linens without special finishes.	Household bleach and vinegar.	Soak in one part bleach to 100 parts water with one tablespoonful vinegar. Rinse thoroughly, then wash.
c) white, drip-dry fabrics.	Hydrogen peroxide solution.	Soak in one part hydrogen peroxide (20 volume) and nine parts water until staining has cleared. Rinse thoroughly then wash in the usual way.
Nail varnish	Amyl Acetate for all fabrics (INF).	Absorbent pad method.
Nicotine (Tobacco juice).	Methylated spirit. (INF) (Benzine for acetate or 'Tricel'). (INF).	Absorbent pad method.
Non-washable ink	Oxalic acid solution. (For white cottons and linens only).	See method (b) under iron mould.
Paint: Emulsion	Water	Emulsion paint splashes sponged immediately with cold water will quickly be removed. Dried stains are pemanent.
Paint: Oil	Turpentine or Amyl Acetate. (INF).	Absorbent pad method.
Perspiration: Fresh stains	Ammonia. **Do not inhale the fumes.**	Damp with water, then hold over an open bottle of household ammonia.
Perspiration: Old stains	White vinegar	Sponge with white vinegar, rinse thoroughly, then wash in usual way.
'Plasticine' Modelling clay	Proprietary grease solvent or lighter fuel. (INF).	Scrape or brush off as much as possible. Apply solvent with absorbent pad method – wash to remove final traces.
Scorch: a) Light marks		Light stains will sometimes respond to treatment as for Group 1 – washable stains.
	Glycerine	If persistent, moisten with water and rub glycerine into the stained area. Wash through. Residual marks may respond to soaking in hydrogen peroxide solution.
b) Heavy marks	Heavy scorch marks that have damaged the fibres cannot be removed.	
Shoe polish	Glycerine and proprietary grease solvent	Lubricate stain with glycerine, then use solvent with absorbent pad method or follow manufacturer's instructions. Wash to remove final traces.

Type of stain	Solvent	Method
Sun tan oil	Proprietary grease solvent	Absorbent pad method or follow manufacturer's instructions.
Tar	Eucalyptus oil, Proprietary grease solvent, Benzine or lighter fuel. (NF).	Scrape off surplus, then apply solvent with absorbent pad method. Rinse and wash as soon as possible.
Verdigris (green stains from copper pipes, etc).		Treat as iron mould.

Special Note: Cotton garments with flame-resistant finishes must **not** be treated with household (chlorine) bleach or hydrogen peroxide in stain removal treatment, since this may impair the finish.

Keep solvents securely closed, labelled and out of children's reach.

Chapter 37

Care labelling in the UK

To help housewives all over the country to know what washing conditions should be followed, the Home Laundering Consultative Council was formed from representatives of washing powder and washing machine manufacturers and the textile trade. The Council determined eight washing processes known as the British Textile Care Labelling Scheme and although this scheme has been superseded by a later more universal system, garment labels and washing machine controls and instructions produced under the eight British Codes will still be in evidence.

As from January 1974, a new system, the result of negotiations between the Home Laundering Consultative Council and the International Care Labelling Symposium, came into being. This is known as **The International Textile Care Labelling Code,** and the eleven wash codes determined under this system are reproduced in detail .

What the symbols mean

The wash tub symbol indicates a particular washing process most appropriate to a fabric or group of fabrics. It recommends:
The maximum safe washing temperature.
The amount of agitation during the wash.
The method of water extraction.

Agitation times

Maximum wash – means the longest agitation time for any machine as defined by the machine manufacturers.
Medium wash – is 40–60% of the maximum time.
Minimum wash – is 20–30% of the maximum time.
Hand wash – apply the label instructions as to the vigour of the wash to the particular circumstances. For fabric groups 6, 7 and 8 do not rub – squeeze the suds gently through the garment.

Water extraction

Instructions for this are in the main self-explanatory. It advises whether:
A cold rinse before spinning would be beneficial;
A long or short spin or no spinning or wringing is needed.
Note – Short Spin is the minimum spinning time as defined by the manufacturers for their appliance – e.g. 15 seconds only for man-made fibre fabrics, to avoid creasing.
When in doubt, spin-dry for the time necessary to remove surplus moisture only.

Other symbols within the International system

Bleaching

 A triangle is the symbol used to indicate that bleach may be used.

 Sometimes the triangle contains the letters 'Cl' which stands for chlorine. It therefore means a household (chlorine) bleach such as 'Domestos'.

 If the symbol is crossed out, this means that household (chlorine)

bleach must **not** be used. If this instruction is ignored the fabric/finish/dye could be seriously affected.

Dry cleaning

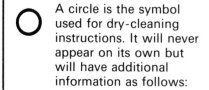

A circle is the symbol used for dry-cleaning instructions. It will never appear on its own but will have additional information as follows:

Articles normal for dry-cleaning in all solvents.

Articles normal for dry-cleaning in perchloro-ethylene, white spirit, Solvent 113 and Solvent 11.

Articles normal for dry-cleaning in white spirit or Solvent 113.

Do **not** dry-clean.

Ironing

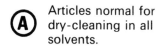

This symbol is used to provide ironing instructions. The number of dots within the symbol is varied to indicate the correct temperature setting, as follows:

One dot = cool.

Two dots = warm.

Threee dots = hot.

Crossed out = **do not iron.**

Drying

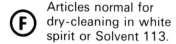

The vast majority of textile articles can safely be tumble dried. Care labels may be used to

indicate either that tumble drying is the optimum drying method for a particular article, or that tumble drying should not be used if the article is likely to be harmed by this treatment.

Tumble drying beneficial.

Do **not** tumble dry.

In cases where the tumble drying prohibition symbol is used, any special positive instructions, such as 'dry flat' for heavier weight knitwear, should be given in words.

Explanation of drying symbols used by other countries

Articles can be tumble-dried.

Drip drying is recommended.

Hang = line-dry.

Dry flat.

Mixed fabric group loads

Ideally fabric groups should not be mixed to make up a wash-load. Unless care is taken it does increase the risk of shrinkage, or dye contamination and discoloration of white things (particularly nylon) from articles which prove non-colourfast under the wash conditions. However, if for convenience or for the sake of economy, there is no alternative, always select the mildest wash conditions and use the following table as a guide:

Fabric codes 1 and 2 together – wash as code 2.
Fabric codes 3 and 4 together – wash as code 4.
Fabric codes 6 and 7 together – wash as code 6.
However, woollen garments must not be rubbed or hand wrung, as

this could distort the fibre. White nylon or articles from codes 5 and 8 should always be washed alone.

Fabric conditioning

No matter how thoroughly clothes are rinsed, after repeated washing and rinsing they gradually lose their bulk and softness. Fabric conditioner in the final rinse untangles matted fibres restoring the natural bulk and bounce to the fabric. But fabric conditioner is not only about softness on towels and woollens, it is about care for all your wash.

Special note on velvet

Velvet is a construction term, not a fibre. It may be silk, cotton or an acetate/nylon blend, e.g., 'Tricelon'. For best results look for the wash-care label and follow the instructions faithfully. If in doubt, dry-clean.

Soft furnishings in velvet weave, e.g., dralon – it is helpful to remove surface dust with a vacuum cleaner or soft brush. 'Dralon' velvet is not washable. It can be cleaned with a dry-foam shampoo. Avoid saturating cotton backing, vacuum or brush foam off when dry. When dry-cleaning, state fibre content.

Flame-retardant fabrics and finishes

Apart from nylon and wool, which are regarded as being of low flammability, there are two ways of giving fabrics flame-retardant properties:
(a) by the application to cotton fabrics of a special finish such as 'Proban', 'Pyrovatex', 'Timonox'. Also in certain cases to wool, though this as yet is not being widely used for apparel purposes.
(b) by the modification of the fibre itself, e.g., fibres like acrylic but with modified properties. The generic term for these is modacrylic, e.g., 'Teklan' or Monsanto's modacrylic. They are

inherently flame retardant.

The appropriate washing codes for the above are:

 Cotton

Wool

 Modacrylics

Important

Flame-retardant fabrics, e.g., modacrylics or fabrics with a flame-retardant finish must not be bleached, or soaked in any washing product.

Fabrics with a flame-retardant finish must not be washed in soap or non-automatic powder as soap can mask the properties of the finish. Other types of washing product, including automatic powder may be used with safety. Rinse very thoroughly.

Hand care

To get the best results in the hand wash make sure the powder is thoroughly dissolved before washing and the clothes thoroughly rinsed afterwards.

After each wash by hand, rinse your hands and dry them thoroughly. People with sensitive or damaged skin should pay particular attention to the instructions for use and avoid prolonged contact with the washing instructions.

If there is no wash care label on the garment, use the following A-Z to find the right fabric group code and full wash-care instructions.

'Special finish' labels

e.g. 'machine washable wool' — Sometimes the finish given to a fabric changes its washability. Where there is no wash-care guidance provided, check the name of the finish in the following A-Z to see whether there are any special care instructions.

No label provided

If you know what the fabric is, check the washing instructions in the A-Z. If in doubt wash under the mildest conditions, i.e., use warm 40°C suds only; do not soak; wash through quickly and gently; rinse thoroughly; blot off surplus moisture with a towel and dry carefully. If washing by machine choose the gentlest programme. If ironing seems appropriate, use a cool iron.

Labels with unfamiliar symbols

These will be found detailed.

Wash for the fabric, never mind the shape!

Remember always that it is the fabric and its construction rather than the type of article that decides the washing treatment. A polyester shirt will be grouped with a textured polyester suit, a small boy's polyester/'Viloft' trousers and his sister's polyester blouse. They are all different shapes and sizes but all will be washed as polyester requires, in hand-hot suds with cold rinsing and a short spin.

Different fabrics require different washing temperatures and agitation times. So ignore the *shape* of the article and concern yourself only with what it is made of and then wash it according to the appropriate Care Labelling Code and follow any special notes in the following A-Z.

Special guidance

Blends and mixtures

A *blend fabric* is one which has been woven or knitted from yarn made by the blending of two of more fibres, prior to the yarn being spun. A *mixture fabric* is one where two or more different yarns are used during weaving or

knitting (e.g., a nylon warp woven into a viscose or cotton weft). In both cases the fibre which needs the milder treatment influences the wash conditions suitable for the fabric. For example a polyester/wool blend should only be washed in warm suds, because of the wool content; polyester/cotton and acrylic/cotton are both washed at temperatures lower than the maximum for cotton. If in doubt, wash as for the fibre requiring the milder treatment.

Colour fastness

Test for colour fastness by damping a piece of the hem or seam allowance and iron a piece of dry white fabric on to it. If any colour blots off, wash the article separately, in very cool suds, and rinse at once in cold water. Put to dry immediately. If the colour is very loose, dry cleaning may be advisable (check the label).

Soaking

There are occasions when heavily soiled or stained articles benefit from a soak before washing, particularly those included in fabric group code 1. Before soaking any coloured article it is important to make sure that:
The dye is fast to soaking – if in doubt do not soak;
The washing powder is completely dissolved before putting in the articles;
The water temperature is not too high for the fabric or the dye;
The article is not **bunched up** – it should be left as free as possible;
White and coloured articles are not soaked together – this is especially necessary where white nylon is concerned as nylon stockings and tights, for example, are seldom fast to soaking for long periods;
The articles do not have metal buttons or metal fasteners – soaking can encourage iron mould (brown stains).
Articles made from wool or silk or

from fabric with a flame-retardant finish, whether white or coloured, should *never be soaked in washing products of any type.*

The International Textile Care Labelling Code

Symbol	Washing Temperature Machine	Hand	Agitation	Rinse	Spinning Wringing	Fabric	Benefits
1 95'	very hot 95°C to boil	hand hot 50°C or boil	maximum	normal	normal	White cotton and linen articles without special finishes	Ensures whiteness and stain removal
2 60'	hot 60°C	hand hot 50°C	maximum	normal	normal	Cotton, linen or viscose articles without special finishes where colours are fast at 60°C	Maintains colours
3 60'	hot 60°C	hand hot 50°C	medium	cold	short spin or drip dry	White nylon, white polyester/cotton mixture	Prolongs whiteness- minimises creasing
4 50	hand hot 50°C	hand hot 50°C	medium	cold	short spin or drip dry	Coloured nylon; polyester; cotton and viscose articles with special finishes; acrylic/cotton mixtures; coloured polyester/cotton	Safeguards colour and finish – minimises creasing
5 40'	warm 40°C	warm 40°C	maximum	normal	normal	Cotton, linen or viscose articles where colours are fast at 40°C but not at 60°C	Safeguards the colour fastness
6 40'	warm 40°C	warm 40°C	minimum	cold	short spin	Acrylics; acetate and triacetate, including mixtures with wool; polyester/wool blends	Preserves colour and shape – minimises creasing
7 40'	warm 40°C	→warm 40°C	minimum do not rub	normal	normal spin do not hand wring	Wool, including blankets and wool mixtures with cotton or viscose silk	Keeps colour, size and handle
8 30'	cool 30°C	cool 30°C	minimim	cold	short spin do not hand wring	Silk and printed acetate fabrics with colours not fast at 40°C	Prevents colour loss
9 95'	very hot 95°C boil	hand hot 50°C or boil	medium	cold	drip dry	Cotton articles with special finishes capable of being boiled but requiring drip-drying	Prolongs whiteness, retains special crease-resistant finish

 Do not machine wash

Do not wash

Expanded description of washing temperatures

100°C	Boil	Self-explanatory.	**50°C**	Hand-hot	As hot as the hands can bear.
95°C	Very hot	Water heated to near boiling temperature.	**40°C**	Warm	Pleasantly warm to the hand.
60°C	Hot	Hotter than the hand can bear. The temperature of water coming from many domestic hot taps.	**30°C**	Cool	Feels cool to the touch.

Changes in wash coding – October 1987

From October 1987 a change in the clothes labelling was introduced. Shown here is a comparison chart between old and new styles. This should help in the transition period when you will have garments bearing both types of labelling. The idea is to give more information on the garment itself, to aid washing and whether or not to mix loads, etc. In the long run, such information will be most helpful and I believe welcomed by all.

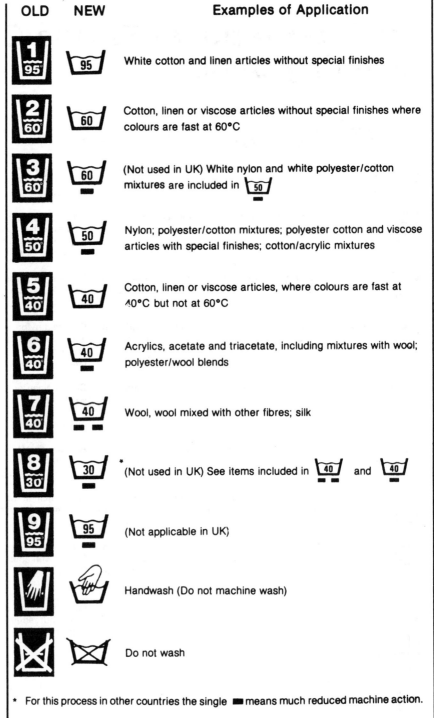

OLD **NEW** **Examples of Application**

White cotton and linen articles without special finishes

Cotton, linen or viscose articles without special finishes where colours are fast at 60°C

(Not used in UK) White nylon and white polyester/cotton mixtures are included in

Nylon; polyester/cotton mixtures; polyester cotton and viscose articles with special finishes; cotton/acrylic mixtures

Cotton, linen or viscose articles, where colours are fast at 40°C but not at 60°C

Acrylics, acetate and triacetate, including mixtures with wool; polyester/wool blends

Wool, wool mixed with other fibres; silk

* (Not used in UK) See items included in   and

(Not applicable in UK)

Handwash (Do not machine wash)

Do not wash

* For this process in other countries the single ■■ means much reduced machine action.

MIXING WASH LOADS

As a general guide you can mix wash labels without a bar provided you wash at the lowest temperature shown.

e.g. ⌐60⌐ and ⌐40⌐ can be washed together at 40°C.

Likewise, you can mix wash labels with and without a bar provided that, again, you wash at the lowest temperature, BUT you must also reduce the washing action.

e.g. ⌐60⌐ and ⌐40⌐ can be washed together at 40°C at a reduced action.

Articles with ⌐40⌐ must be washed as wool at a much reduced action.

REMEMBER "wash separately" means what it says.

EXAMPLES OF THE NEW LABEL FORMATS

⌐50⌐ Wash as Synthetics	MACHINE	HAND WASH
	Hand hot medium wash	Hand hot
	Cold rinse. Short spin or drip-dry	
⚠ (do not bleach)	DO NOT USE CHLORINE BLEACH	
◯ (tumble dry)	MAY BE TUMBLE DRIED	
⊿ (iron)	WARM	
Ⓟ	DRY CLEANABLE	

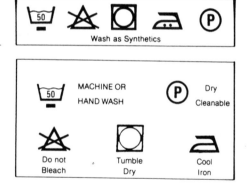

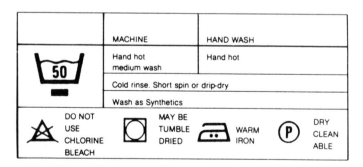

What it's called	What it is	Special notes	Wash code	Ironing notes
A				
Acetate	A cellulose derivative **fibre** fairly warm, soft, light, mothproof. Widely used in mixture fabrics.	Handle gently when wet. Take care with stain solvents.	[6/40] or [8/30]	Slightly and evenly damp on wrong side with **cool** iron.
'Acrilan'	See acrylics.		[6/40]	
Acrylics	Acrylic fibres have a warm soft handle yet are strong and hard-wearing. Good crease recovery. Do not shrink. Mothproof. Not affected by mildew.	Treat heavy knitted articles carefully when wet to avoid stretching.	[6/40]	**Cool** iron if required. To avoid stretching a knitted fabric it is often best to iron dry.
Actifresh	A bacteriostatic finish which prevents bacterial growth on synthetic fibres.		[6/40] or [4/50]	
Angora	Natural **fibre** obtained from the Angora rabbit. Warm, soft wool, with very fluffy surface.	Hand wash with care.	[hand wash]	Optional. **Warm** iron over **damp** cloth, or steam iron. Brush with teasel brush when **dry** to raise the surface.
B				
'Banion'	A proprietary process for giving bulk, moderate stretch and extra warmth to synthetic thermoplastic yarns.		[3/60] White nylon [4/50] Others	**Warm** iron on **dry** fabric if necessary.
Bonded Fabrics	See laminates.			
Brushed Fabrics	Fabrics that have been brushed and the surface raised to provide extra warm handle e.g., brushed nylon, brushed viscose.	According to fabric. Check label.		Optional, **cool** iron when **dry**.
C				
Cashmere	Natural **fibre** consisting of downy undercoat of Tibetan cashmere goat. Very soft, warm handle; quickly felts with careless or over-vigorous washing.	Hand wash with care.	[hand wash]	Press on **wrong** side with **warm** iron under **damp** cloth to restore size, or use steam iron.
Cling Resist Nylon: 'Counterstat'	Nylon wth anti-static properties. Reduces 'cling' and 'riding up'. See nylon.			
Chloro fibres	See PVC			
'Clevyl T'	Trilobal chloro **fibre**.			
'Clydella'	A mixture **fabric** of natural fibres, wool and cotton woven together; lightweight, warm, ideal for baby wear.		[7/40]	Optional, **Warm** iron on **wrong** side when **damp**.
Corduroy	Cut-weft pile fabric with corded effect. Usually cotton.	Check label. Wash deep and bright colours separately. **Drip-dry**.	[4/50] [6/40]	**Do not iron.** If necessary remove creases by steaming.
Cotton	Natural **fibre**; strong, hard-wearing; stronger wet than dry, withstands vigorous washing processes without damage.		[1/95] W [2/60] C	**Hot** iron when **damp**.
'Courtelle'	See acrylics.			
'Crimplene'	See polyester. Textured 'Terylene' filament yarns which combine bulk with low stretch and offer excellent easy-care properties.	Used in men's wear and stretch covers.		

What it's called	What it is	Special notes	Wash code	Ironing notes
D				
Damask	An elaborately woven **fabric** used for furnishings, table linen, towels may be linen, cotton or viscose.	Creases easily, may be starched.		**Hot** iron on **right** side.
'Dacron'	See polyester.			
Denim	A construction term for a twill weave **fabric,** often cotton or cotton blends.	Not all denim is colourfast. Check label. Allow for shrinkage.	[1/95]W [2/60] [5/40]C	**Hot** iron when **damp.**
'Dicel'	See acetate.			
'Diolen'	See polyester.			
'Dralon'	See acrylics.	All Draylon fabrics are washable except woven velvet which must be dry-cleaned.		
Drip-dry cotton	Cotton which has been specially processed to give an easy-care, crease-resistant, minimum iron or non-iron finish.		[4/50]	Optional. **Warm** iron when **dry.**
'Durable Press'	See Permanent Press.			
'Dylan'	Proprietary process to impart shrink-resistance to wool. In some cases gives machine washability. Check with label.		[7/40]	Optional. **Warm** iron over a damp cloth; or use a steam iron.
'Dynel'	Modascrylic **fibre.** See flame retardant fibres.	Often used in fur fabrics.	[6/40]	
E				
Egyptian Cotton	Fine quality natural cotton **fibre**, made into closely woven cloth from Egypt; extremely hard wearing.		[1/95]W [2/60]C	**Hot** iron on **wrong** side when **damp.**
Elastane Fibres	Man-made stretch **fibres** with high rate of stretch recovery. Soft to the touch, light in weight. Used with other fibres for swimwear and foundation garments.	Wash according to other fabrics in weave, but **not** above 4. Check label.		**Do not iron.**
'Everglaze'	See glazed cotton.			
'Evalan'	Cellulosic, modified viscose **fibre**. Often blended with nylon, wool and acrylics.	Wash according to other fabrics in weave but **not** above 4. Evlan is most widely used in carpets but is used in some apparel.		
F				
'Fibreglass'	See Fibreglass.			
Fibreglass	**Fabric** woven from fine glass filaments. Resistant to bacteria, completely flame-proof. Drapes well. Does not sag or stretch.	Handle gently. Liable to fray if machine-washed. Abrasion can cause damage to the surface and loss of colour. **Drip dry.**	[hand wash]	**Do not iron.**
Fixaform'	See Permanent Press. A proprietary process which enables garments to retain pleats and shape.			

What it's called	What it is	Special notes	Wash code	Ironing notes
F (cond.)				
Flame Retardant Fabrics		Do not soak or bleach or boil.	[4/50] [6/40]	If necessary press **lightly on wrong** side whilst slightly damp. **Cool** iron.
Flame Retardant Finishes		Non-soap detergent wash only. Do not use soaps or soap products. Rinse carefully. **Never** soak or bleach.	[4/50]	**Cool** iron.
Flannelette	Flannel, a lightweight imitation of wool made from cotton or viscose mixtures.	Check label for colours. If made from any other fabric, wash according to fabric type. Check label.	[1/95] W [2/60] [5/40] C	**Hot** iron when slightly **damp**. As for fabric.
Foam Backs	**Fabrics** to which a layer of polyurethane or polyester foam has been bonded to the back of the face fabric to give warmth without weight and preserve shape.	Not all foam backs are suitable for home washing. If in doubt 'dry clean'. Washable foam backs should be laundered according to face fabrics. Always check label.		Iron according to face fabric.
G				
Glazed Cotton	Cotton with a special finish. Permanently glazed cotton will retain the high gloss; others lose their sheen on washing.		[4/50]	**Hot** iron on **wrong** side when **damp** Finish by polishing on **right** side.
Grosgrain Georgette Gaberdine	Names of particular types of weaves. May be silk, nylon, viscose, polyester, wool used in clothing fabrics.	Wash according to fibre type. Check label.		Iron according to fabric type.
H				
'Helenca'	A proprietary process used to impart high stretch to yarns such as nylon and polyester where a good stretch fit is desirable. Used for slacks and swimwear.		[3/60] White nylon [4/50] Others	**Warm** iron when **dry**, if necessary.
K				
Kenekalon 'Kopratron'	Modacrylic **fibre**. Trade name for 'Permanent or Durable Press' fabrics.		[4/50]	
L				
Lambswool	A natural **fibre**. Fine graded, high quality wool with exceptionally soft handle.	Hand wash with care.	[hand wash]	Press lightly with **warm** iron under **damp** cloth; or use steam iron. Brush up pile when dry.
Laminates	Two or more layers of fabrics bonded together to give strength, preserve shape, provide warmth without needing to line garment.	Not all laminates are suitable for home-washing. If in doubt 'dry-clean'. Washable laminates should be laundered according to face fabrics. Always check label.		Iron, if necessary, according to face fabric.
'Lastex'	A natural stretch yarn made from extruded rubber, used in corsetry, swimwear, ski wear.	Check garment label.		**Do not** iron.

What it's called	What it is	Special notes	Wash code	Ironing notes
Linen	Natural yarn **fibre** from flax. Very strong, washes and wears well.	Can be washed and ironed at high temperatures. Withstands bleaching and boiling if white.	[1/95] W [2/60] C	**Hot** iron when **damp**.
'Lirelle'	See polyester.			
'Lurex'	Proprietary name for specially processed metallic **threads** of various types to suit the yarn with which it is incorporated.	Wash as main fabric. Dry-clean where it is recommended.		**Warm** iron.
'Lycra'	See Elastane fibres.			
M				
'Marglass'	See Fibreglass.			
Minimum-iron	A finish obtained by special processing or weaving to impart easy-care properties and to eliminate ironing as far as possible.	According to fabric type. **Drip-dry.** Check label.	[3/60] [4/50] [6/40]	**Warm** iron when **dry** if necessary.
'Mitrelle'	Made from ICI **fibres**. Silk-like polyester yarns.			
Modacrylic	Class of man-made **fibre** contains 30–80% acrylonitrile, inherently flame retardant.	Check label.	[4/50]	**Cool** iron if necessary.
Modal	Viscose in modified form with improved wet strength, used mainly in blends with cotton or polyester.	Check label.	[2/60] [5/40]	**Hot** iron when **damp**. Warm iron if necessary for polyester blends.
Mohair	A natural **fibre** from the Angora goat. 'Long-haired' wool with exceptional warmth in wear.	Hand wash only.	[hand wash]	Press on **wrong** side under **damp** cloth with **warm** iron; or use steam iron. Brush up pile when dry.
Monsanto's Modacrylic	Modacrylic **fibre**. See flame-retardant fabrics. Used for pile fabrics, curtains, bedspreads.		[6/40]	
N				
Nylon	Strong, versatile synthetic **fibre**. Mothproof; quick-drying, with good abrasion-resistance. Tends to build up static electricity and attracts dirt. Is 'low-flam'.		[3/60] W [4/50] C	**Warm** iron when **dry** if necessary.
P				
'Perlon'	See nylon.			
Permanent Press	A technique for giving permanent shape and creases to garments. Very suitable for men's trousers, rainwear, ski wear and stretch slacks.	According to fabric. **Do not wring.**	[4/50] [6/40]	Not necessary.
Polyester	Man-made fibre; very strong and hard wearing. Takes permanent pleats well, does not shrink or stretch. Mothproof. Mixes well with other fibres.	Attracts greasy soiling wash regularly.	[4/50]	**Warm** iron when **dry** if necessary.
Polyester/Cotton	A blend of polyester and cotton yarns, giving the appearance and handle of cotton combined with the 'easy-care' and smooth drying of polyester.	Do not allow to become heavily soiled before washing.	[3/60] W [4/50] C	**Warm** iron when **dry** if necessary.

What it's called	What it is	Special notes	Wash code	Ironing notes
P (cond.)				
'Proban'	See flame-retardant finishes.	Non-soap detergent only. **Do not use soap.**	[4/50]	Cool iron.
P.V.C.	Polyvinyl chloride. A man-made thermo-plastic **fibre** which is chemically stable and non-flammable (i.e. does not burn without assistance). Water-repellent. Strong, wet or dry, but shrinks over 70°C. Softens at higher temperatures.	Soft fabrics. Used widely in upholstery and protective clothing. For coats and raincoats sponge only.	[6/40]	Do not iron.
'Pyrovaex'	See flame retardant finishes.	Non-soap detergent only. **Do not use soap.**	[4/50]	Cool iron.
Q				
'Quiana'	See nylon. 'Quiana' has a silk-like texture and soft handle.			
R				
'Rhonel'	See Triacetate.			
'Rhovyl'	See P.V.C.		[6/40]	
'Rigmel'	A proprietary finish used to impart shrink-resistance to cotton.		[1/95]W [2/60]C	Hot iron when damp.
S				
'Sanforized'	Special finish giving shrink-resistance to cottons and fabrics likely to be washed regularly.	Wash as fabric type.		Iron as fabric type.
'Sarille'	Modified crimpled staple viscose. giving wool-like properties and drape. Used in dress-fabrics and blankets.		[5/40] damp.	Hot iron when slightly and evenly
'Scotchgard'	A water and oil repellent finish for clothing and furnishing fabrics, suitable for home washing or dry-cleaning.	Wash as fabric. Rinse very thoroughly. **Drip-dry.**		**Warm** iron if necessary.
Shantung	Wild silk with a slub incorporated in the weave – see silk.			
Silk and Wild silk	Natural protein **fibre** from the silkworm. Very soft handle with luxurious appearance. Creases easily but creases fall out. Expensive. Used in luxury fabrics.	Rinse thoroughly. Dry gently.	[7/40] [8/30]	**Warm** iron when slightly and evenly **damp**; wild silk **cool** iron when **dry**.
'Spanzelle'	See Elastane fibres. Spanzelle has been withdrawn. May still be found in textiles for some time.			
'Superwash' Wool	Now known as 'Machine Washable Wool'. A polymer process giving shrink-resistance to wool. In most cases also imparts machine washability whilst retaining softness. Check with label.		[7/40]	**Warm** iron over a **damp** cloth or use steam iron.
T				
'Teklan'	See flame-retardant fabrics. A Modacrylic fibre.		[6/40]	
'Tendrelle'	See Nylon.			

What it's called	What it is	Special notes	Wash code	Ironing notes
'Tergal'	See Polyester.			
'Terital'	See Polyester.			
'Teryline'	See Polyester.			
'Tetron'	See Polyester.			
'Timonox'	See Flame Retardant Finishes.	Synthetic detergent only. **Do not use soap.**	[4/50]	**Cool** iron.
'Trevira'	see Polyester.			
'Triacetate'	Man-made cellulosic derivative **fibre,** easy to match, does not shrink or stretch. More robust in wash and wear than acetate. Good drape, silky handle.	For pleated garment – check label.	[6/40]	**Cool** iron when **damp.**
'Tricel'	See Triacetate.			
Trilobal	Technical term to describe fibres with a rounded triangular cross-section which gives improved handle and appearance.			
Tussore	Wild silk incorporating a slub in the weave – see silk.			
U				
'Ultron'	Nylon with anti-static properties. Reduces 'cling' and 'riding-up.' See nylon.			
V				
Velvet	See Special Notes.			
'Verel'	Modacrylic staple **fibre** for pile fabrics and carpets.			
'Viloft'	A tubular viscose **fibre** with high bulk and extra absorbency usually mixed with polyester or acrylic.	Washes well often used in leisure garments because of comfort characteristics. Used extensively in sportswear, underwear, including thermal.	[4/50]	
Viscose	Widely used man-made cellulosic **fibre** used on its own, as a mixture fabric or blended with other yarns. Pleasant handle and drapes well; good dyeing properties. (Formerly rayon or viscose rayon).		[2/60]	**Hot** iron on **wrong** side when **damp.**
'Viyella'	Mixture **fabric** of 55% lamb's wool and 45% cotton with a warm, soft handle, suitable for babies' and children's wear. More recently developed for top fashion clothes.		[7/40]	**Warm** iron on **wrong** side whilst slightly **damp.**
W				
Water	**Fabrics** given special finish to confer some resistance to water penetration.	Avoid detergents. Wash according to fabric type in soap powder. Rinse very thoroughly. **Dry-dry.** Check label.		**Warm** iron if necessary.
Wool	Natural **fibre** from the sheep; available in several qualities. Warm, soft handle.	Hand wash unless article carries machine label.	[hand wash] [7/40]	**Warm** iron under **damp** cloth or steam iron.

Chapter 38

Jargon

Amp – Short for ampere. Used to measure the flow or electricity through a circuit or appliance.

Armature – Wire wound centre of brush motor.

Bi-metal – Two different metals which have been joined together. When heated the strip bends in a known direction.

Boss – Protection around entry point.

Burn-out – Overheated part of item.

Bus bar – An electrical conductor.

Cable – Conductors covered with a protective semi-rigid insulating sheath, used to connect the individual components within a wiring system.

Carbon face (seal) – Watertight flat surface seal.

Centrifugal – Force that increases with rotation causing movement away from its centre.

Circuit – Any complete path for an electric current, allowing it to pass along a 'live' conductor to where it is needed and then to return to its source along a 'neutral' conductor.

Clamp band – Large adjustable clip used for holding door boot.

Closed circuit – A normal circuit that allows power to pass through.

Collet – Tapered sleeve of two or more parts designed to grip a shaft passed through its centre.

Commutator – Copper segment on motor armature.

Component – Individual parts of the machine, i.e., pump, valves, motors, are all components.

Conductor – The metallic current-carrying 'cores' within cable or flex.

Consumer Unit – Unit governing the supply of electricty to all circuits and containing a main on-off switch and fuses or circuit breakers protecting the circuits emanating from it.

Contact – Point at which switch makes contact.

Continuity – Electrical path with no break.

Corbin – Type of spring hose clip.

Damped – To have reduced movement of suspension, i.e., reduce oscillation of tub unit during distribute and spin cycles.

Dispenser – Compartment that holds detergent ready for use.

Dispenser hose – Hose that supplies the tub with detergent and water from the dispenser compartment.

Distribute – To balance load by centrifugal force, i.e., a set speed calculated to even out wash load prior to faster spin.

Door boot – Flexible seal between door and tub.

Door gasket – Flexible seal between door and tub.

Door seal – Flexible seal between door and tub.

Drift – Soft metal rod used for bearing removal.

E.L.C.B. – Earth leakage circuit breaker – see R.C.C.B.

E.M.F. – Source of energy that can cause a current to flow in a circuit or device.

Early – Machine not currently on the market.

Energize (Energise) – To supply power to.

Energized (Energised) – Having power supplied to.

Flowchart – Method of following complicated steps in a logical fashion.

Functional test – To test machine on a set programme.

Garter ring – Large elastic band or spring used to secure door boot.

Grommet fitting – Method of fitting hoses, etc., requiring no clips.

Harness – electrical wiring within a machine.

Hertz – Periodic cycle of one second, i.e., cycles per second.

'Hunting' – Oscillating.

Impeller – The blades of the water pump.

Insulation – Material used to insulate a device or a region.

Isolate – To disconnect from the electrically supply and water supply, etc.

Laminations – Joined metal parts of stator.

Late – Current machine on market.

Lint – Fluff from clothing that may cause a small blockage.

Live – Supply current carrying conductor.

Make – 1. Manufacturer's name.
2. When a switch makes contact it is said to make.

Microprocessor – Miniature integrated circuit containing programme information.

Miniature Circuit Breaker – (MCB) a device used instead of fuses to isolate a circuit if fault/overload occurs.

Neutral – Return current carrying conductor.

O.O.B. – Out of balance detection system.

Open-circuit – Circuit that is broken, i.e., will not let any power through.

Outer casing – Cabinet, "shell" of the machine.

P.S.I. – Measurement of water pressure, pounds per square inch, e.g. 38 p.s.i.

Pawl – Pivoted lever designed to engage ratchet gearing.

Porous – Item that allows water to pass through.

Potentiometer – Variable resistance device.

Processor – Main central processing component of computer control circuitry.

Programmer – See Timer.

R.C.C.B. – Residual current circuit breaker (also known as R.C.D.)

R.C.D. – Residual current device. See also – E.L.C.B. and R.C.C.B.

Reciprocating – Mechnanical action of backwards and forwards movement.

Reverse polarity – A situation where live and neutral feeds have reversed, e.g., connected incorrectly at supply, socket or plug.

Ribbon cable – Flat cable used for low voltage P.C.B. connections.

Rotor – Central part of an induction motor.

Schematic diagram – Theoretical diagram.

Seal – Piece of pre-shaped rubber that usually fits into a purpose built groove or between two surfaces, therefore creating a watertight seal when subjected to pressure.

Sealant – Rubber substance used for ensuring watertight joints.

Shell – Outer of machine.

Spades – Connections on wires or components – remove gently.

Stat – Abbreviation of thermostat.

Stator – Electrical winding on motor.

Terminal block – A method of connecting wires together safely.

T.O.C. – Thermal overload cut-out. At a pre-set temperature, the T.O.C. will break electrical circuit to whatever it is in circuit with, i.e., prevents motors, etc., overheating.

Thermistor – A semi-conductor device, the resistance of which is affected by temperatures.

Thermostat – Device used to monitor temperature.

Thyristor – Electronic switching device.

Timer – Programme switch.

Triac – Electronic switching device.

Volt – Unit of electrical pressure (potential) difference. In most British homes the mains voltage is 240v.

Volatile (when relating to computer control applications) – Unable to store information when power is turned off.

Non-Volatile (when relating to computer control applications) – Retains information for a set period even with power turned off.

Watt – Unit of power consumed by an appliance or circuit, the product of the mains voltage and the current drawn (in amps). 1000W = 1 Kilowatt (KW).